"Moses spake unto the Lord saying, . . . Tell Me concerning this earth and the inhabitants thereof, . . ."

—Moses 1:36

Tell Me

by Polly Block

Twenty-four Heartwarming Stories

(with accompanying activities)

OTHER TITLES BY AUTHOR

A SUPERIOR ALTERNATIVE: CHILDBIRTH AT HOME
POLLY'S BIRTH BOOK: OBSTETRICS FOR THE HOME
AARON, YOU'RE AWESOME

<u>Nurturing The Spirit Series:</u>
BENEATH A PRAIRIE BUSH
THE CROSSING
THE FASTEST BUGGY HORSE IN ALPINE
SHE CARRIED ME ALL THE WAY

A COAL OF FIRE FROM THE HEARTH
THE SONG OF A VOLUNTEER
O JERUSALEM, JERUSALEM

Cover Photo by Waldo Cook

 For information address: Hearthspun Publishers, 475 North 300 West, American Fork, Utah 84003.

Copies may be ordered from the address above: $14.95 plus S/H

DESIGNATION OF READER LEVEL

There are twenty-four stories in this volume. There are four poems. They were all written to be enjoyed by the entire family, but for your convenience each story has been designated a category since some ages will particularly enjoy particular stories.

It is impossible to determine a person's interest level by his age, therefore strictly general terms will represent age groups:

PEDAL PUSHERS PLUS: very young to ten years.
THOSE COMING OF AGE: eleven to eighteen years.
THE DEFENDERS OF THE FAITH: Adults.

If only adults are home for Family Home Evenings there are stories for you. When the neighbor child or grandchildren come to call, you will not have to buy separate books for them. Remember that each story will become a favorite for family get-together. Each volume will become a favorite Christmas or birthday gift for someone you love.

Preface

It is my belief that only truth and divine purpose really matter. The thoughts I find penetrating to the core of matters, kindle a deep love and appreciation in my heart. They may differ from the thoughts of others, or we may find them joining hands. The spirit must direct.

In my effort to assist in the pursuit of the more abundant life, my stories, my earliest recollections, and the interpretation of gospel principles that are woven into this material are mine, and are not meant in any way to stand as doctrines for The Church of Jesus Christ of Latter-day Saints, of which I am a member in good standing. I take full responsibility for the perspective I have taken of the values found in this volume.

The Author.

Dedicated to the

Latter Day Classroom

Found wherever the latter day family meets: under a tree at story time, at the fishing hole with father, in Family Home Evenings, in the private or home school where gospel principles are welcome.

FORWARD

The author was born in mid 1900 in the south where the culture was steeped in strong family/religious influences. Those forces brought steadfastness and loyalty, warmth and humble attitudes toward life.

The economy of the depression deprived our nation of arrogance or elitism for some time. Those qualities were simply removed in the broadest sense. Dire straits had a way of humbling people, nevertheless, there were benefits.

The Good Book reminds us that our land will not prosper if we are in need of pure humility, teachability. Verily the imperative of caring for human life and dignity was imposed upon us. We didn't learn very fast, thus causing severe reverses. This often brought about family cohesiveness, or dissolution. "Making do, or doing without" could have been born there. At once everyone was in the same boat.

All manner of hardships were endured, but the faith, hope, and promise of a better tomorrow overall, stayed the course until better financial times gradually returned.

The storytellers as well as the characters in these accounts were significantly steeped in this unpretentiousness. It is heart warming, in the latter-day classroom, to review their plights and their surrender to "making it work"--a divine endowment of the human spirit. Surviving led to the finding of joy and satisfaction in work whether or not it proved to be lucrative.

Blessed is the individual who truly is grateful for trials; who can appreciate the makings of humility. Blessed is the individual who admits life is better because of growing pains saturated with the ridiculous episodes that become memory makers.

This volume has been prepared for those families who veer from portrayals of hate, violence, hyper-activity and those empty values that leave us meandering in darkness. Indeed the time and age in which we live is fast-paced and geared to the technological. Taking time to sit back and let children view life from a period when there was time to ponder, may be overdue.

Time for our children to savor the learning moments, to taste the sweet and simple steps to reason can be found at the feet of good parents and grandparents whoever and wherever they are.

Thanks to a wonderful, extended family who in the course of their lives inadvertently created and painted these happy word pictures for us.

TELL ME

TABLE OF CONTENTS

PART TWO

A MESSAGE TO STUDENTS

We all love pictures. It is fun to open a book or sit before television and "see" what others want to "tell" us. It is true that when we use as many of our senses as possible, we tend to store memory well. Those senses referred to, are the sense of smell, taste, touch, hearing and sight. We sometimes speak of a sixth sense, one that is more elusive but engendered by the spirit.

When the spirit imprints upon our minds things of the spirit, memory may be even more indelible, and recalled particularly when we are in tune or in need.

THE LATTER-DAY CLASSROOM book, TELL ME, will not use pictures with the text. It is the intention of the author to give the student an extended opportunity to draw pictures of his own from the words or messages he hears, thus building a keen sense with which to accept or reject the message.

Word pictures, if commendable, give the spirit within a chance to connect with the pictures drawn by our own hearts and minds as influenced by Heavenly Father. Directed by the spirit, outside influences, or imposed pictures, may not be as greatly empowered to register or record upon our minds.

THE LATTER-DAY CLASSROOM message to all students is to guard your memory banks well. Do not allow space to be taken by filth or hate or evil. Make your memory bank a happy place to visit, a rich and wonderful source from which to call up direction and thanksgiving.

We certainly may choose to show our eyes good and lovely things in every day life and view those reproduced through camera and on canvass. We certainly must choose good books to read. There, seeds of worthy ideas and messages grow to give the materials we need to build those great pictures in our minds.

Draw pictures with your own words, your own pencil or brush, and share the good things of life with others.

MY EYES

I like for my eyes to look upon things beautiful.

I choose to show my eyes mountains being crowned with billowed mounds, or being swallowed by mists of tears that hang neither up nor down.

I love giving my eyes the chance to watch the morning face of a baby lamb, or the fragile legs of a fawn stepping to the edge of deep wet blue, cradled in the lap of the forest.

My eyes like to find that look in the eyes of young lovers as their car whirls past on an early spring day.

I'm glad my eyes have looked upon the births of children, of mornings, animals, and flowers. Yes, even the quiet demise of mother, from the house she came to live in four score and one years ago.

My eyes revel in dancing over written words that picture places, meet peoples, unveil emotions, praise God.

I liked it when my eyes saw gentleness and patience, covered by thin gray hair in the Holy Land,bent in the labor of wheel chairing a helpless spouse on tour.

Ahh! I showed my eyes all they could behold of the Savior's homeland and His footpaths, and let them look, deeply scanning with the aid of spiritual vision, the Sea of Galilee and the hills of miracles.

My eyes send back hurt when they look upon waste, sin and anger, but I may not shut these out, else my eyes would fall shadow to the light of things beautiful.

From WIND SONGS AND BLUEBONNETS.

PART ONE

NOTES

BEFORE AIR-CONDITIONING

"What made you interested in the days before air-conditioning, Lily?" asked her grandfather.

"Oh, I was complaining that it was too hot to do my assignments today, 'cause, Pappy-Gene, you just can't think or get your work done when you are sweating!"

Lily sighed then asked, "So, guess who has to make a report on what people used to do to cool down--before air-conditioning?"

Lily's grandfather, whose nickname was Pappy-Gene, was visiting from Texas. She found him sitting on a bench by the picnic table under the big silver leaf maple tree in the back yard. Lily's family called it their "Million Dollar Tree" because it's huge branches kept most of the yard shady all day long.

NOTES

Lily lay on her stomach on the cool grass and asked her Grandfather how he had survived living in hot old Texas before air-conditioning.

When Pappy-Gene lived in San Antonio, Texas as a boy, he had a wonderful place to play and keep cool.

" My friend, Arbuth Merkin, and I used to play in the tunnel under the Alamo! It was dark and cool in there."

"What's the Alamo, Pappy-Gene?"

Pappy-Gene couldn't imagine that he, a Texan, had not told his grandchildren in Utah about the Alamo! He briefly explained that it was a very old and famous mission, or church, in San Antonio where some brave soldiers fought the Mexican army many years ago.

"All the Texan soldiers and their friends died in the fierce battle. But their fight helped keep Texas free."

Pappy-Gene explained, "Your seventh great uncle, Sam Houston, led a Texas army to trail the

NOTES

Mexicans and win the war, Lily. After that, everyone remembered the Alamo as a sacred place to honor the dead who fought so bravely at the Battle of The Alamo. Why, I'll bet almost as many people visit the Alamo now as visit Temple Square in Salt Lake City!"

"Wow, Pappy-Gene, I didn't know that!" Lily was impressed.

"Sam Houston went on to become President of the Republic of Texas, and when Texas joined the United States, they made him Governor of the State of Texas."

"My seventh great uncle was a president--and a governor?" Lily was wide-eyed and sat up straight to hear this story.

"Why sure, but that is another story, let's get back to this story." Pappy-Gene continued.

"When I was a boy, my friend's father was caretaker of the small park across the street from the Alamo. Mr. Merkin mowed the lawn and cleaned up the spring house at one end of the park. You see,

NOTES

there was no water in the Alamo, but there was a flowing spring in the little park."

Pap was a good story teller. He took his time and you could just see the pictures coming into his mind as his stories rolled along.

"Long ago, a tunnel was dug from under the Alamo over to the San Pedro Springs. During the hot days of summer, the tunnel was a cool shelter or a cool walk to the spring." Pappy-Gene rubbed his chin, trying to remember details.

"Originally the spring may have been hidden by tall grass and a clump of trees. When the people or the soldiers living in the Alamo needed water, they could secretly obtain it, by going through the tunnel out to the spring."

"In later years," Pappy-Gene explained, "a band stand was built over the spring to protect it, and they piped the water into fountains for visitors to use.

"Mr. Merkin would work in the park and allow Arbuth and me to play in the tunnel, because he knew right where we were and could watch us."

NOTES

"Pappy-Gene, isn't it dangerous to play in tunnels?"

"My goodness, yes! But the City of San Antonio had preserved the tunnel by walling it up with rocks. It was a long time before rain eroded the soil and filled in the tunnel."

"Was the tunnel like a cave?" asked Lily.

"Well, yes. It was over a hundred feet long but when we played in it the ceiling was only about three or four feet high." Pappy-Gene lifted his hand in the air to demonstrate the height.

"It was sort of dark and scary, but that is why we liked it! When we played like we were cowboys, it was a good place to ride our horses into, and hide from the outlaws. If we thought the outlaws were going to come in after us, the spiders would scare them off! We were sure of that, 'cause they scared us!"

Lily's eyes opened wider as she imagined seeing spiders hanging on their webs across the ceiling of the tunnel.

NOTES

Pappy-Gene went on, "It was cooler inside the cave than it was in the park--and we were always bare footed. The soles of our feet were so tough, we could run through stickers or over rocks and never even know it. Shoes cost too much anyway."

Pappy-Gene continued his story of how people dealt with the heat. "I also lived in Luling, Texas, when I was a little older. On the farm the summers were mighty hot, especially when you had to work in the fields all day. We had no thermometers. No radio, and we never saw a newspaper that might predict the weather. There were no promising weather men and I'll bet there were days over a hundred degrees!

"On the farm we came in from the fields about noon. The teams of mules were sweaty and hot. So were we. We took the harnesses off, drew about fifty buckets of water from the well, or so it seemed, and poured it into the water trough. When the teams were through drinking, we would give them a couple of bales of hay. Then we would pull off our shirts,

NOTES

rinse them out in the trough, and hang them on the fence to dry. We even washed our faces in the same water before going to the back porch to get a drink."

"Yuk! I hope you didn't drink from the water trough where the horses drank!" exclaimed Lily with her nose wrinkled up.

"Course not. A big cedar bucket always hung on the back porch. It had brass bands around it and a big gourd dipper hung on a nail above the water pail. Water from a cedar bucket tasted mighty good. I'll bet you have never tasted well water from a cedar bucket, have you, Lily? Do you know what a gourd is?"

"No, Pappy-Gene," confessed Lily, to both questions.

"Gourds grew in the garden and looked like some kinds of squash. We let them dry, then cut off half of the round, ball-like end and took the seeds out. We left the long end on the gourd to use for a handle. Water tastes wonderful from a gourd, Lily."

Lily crossed her legs and leaned up against the

NOTES

Million Dollar Tree's big trunk.

"Well, back to our story. Usually we had beans and cornbread and onions for lunch. My goodness, I can just taste those pinto beans and cornbread," Pappy-Gene dreamed. "When we finished eating, we lay on the shady porch where a gentle breeze sometimes came along. Nearly all homes in the south had porches on two or three sides of their houses. D'you know why?"

"No, why, Pappy-Gene?"

"Because it was usually cooler outside the house if you could sit in the shade. So if you had a porch on several sides of your house you could just move to another porch when the sun caught up with you. And if they had a lot of shade trees too it extended the cool area. The women would shell peas and shuck corn on the porches. Even churn the butter out there sometimes."

"I wondered why people in the south had so many pretty porches." Lily had seen big houses with porches when she went to Texas with her parents.

NOTES

"Then what did you do, Pap?"

We lay on the porch and put our shoes under our heads for pillows."

"Your shoes, Pappy? Weren't they hard?" Lily couldn't imagine this being comfortable, but having your shoes off would be cooler.

"Well, sure. They were hard but we were all dirty and our Ma sure wouldn't let us bring clean pillows out on the porch. It wasn't bad, Lily. It just felt good to be resting for a while--in the shade!"

Pappy-Gene went on, "We slept for about an hour. About two o'clock they would wake us up and we would hear, `Boys, it's time to go.'" Almost as if asking himself, Pappy-Gene asked, "I wonder how we did it?"

"Did what, Pap?" inquired Lily.

"I wonder how we got through such heat, working in the fields all day, right out in the sun? There was no ice, no fan or anything." Then he asked, "Do you think your classroom is that hot, Lily?"

NOTES

"I don't think so, Pappy-Gene, but sometimes--", Lily interrupted herself because here came a question to her mind. "How did people keep their milk from spoiling? I left ours out of the fridge the other morning and by the time I got home from Primary it was sour."

"If you lived in town where they could deliver ice every other day for your pan-dripping ice box, that'd be fine, but out on the farm they put a few jars of milk and some butter in tin buckets then let the buckets down into the well just far enough to touch the water. They tied the ropes to the beams on the overhanging cross-bar up by the pulley that was used to draw the bucket up out of the water. So the buckets would go no deeper and that cold water kept everything cool."

Pappy-Gene watched Lily's eyes to see if she was understanding his "word picture". She had a question as she thought about this, "Didn't bugs get into the milk?"

"Oh, not usually. We'd put a lid on the bucket.

NOTES

Some people built small wooden houses over their springs, then set buckets or pans of food in the cool water that ran through the ditch or on shelves near the water so it would not spoil.

"But do you know what we did?" Pappy-Gene moved into a lawn chair so he could see Lily better. He shifted in his chair with new enthusiasm.

"Finally after someone invented ice cream, about once a month the family brought a hundred pounds of ice out to the farm from town. We wrapped the ice in an old blanket or tow sacks--you call them gunny sacks up here in the Rockies-- we'd put it in the back of the wagon and bring it home and we'd make two or three freezers of ice cream. That helped us cool off on Sunday after church."

"Yummy," Lily licked her lips. "I'll bet you had to eat it all up right away before it melted if you didn't have a fridge, huh, Pappy?"

"Oh, we could handle that all right! We put a gunny sack or two over the hand-crank freezer and it would last for quite a while."

NOTES

It was fun for Pappy-Gene to remember the good old days. It was fun for Lily to imagine her grandfather, Pappy-Gene, ever being a young boy.

"Did you get to sit on the tow sacks while someone turned the crank on the ice cream freezer, Pap?"

"Now that was something that kept us cool for a while. We used to fight over who got to sit on the ice cream freezer when I was a boy."

Lily thought living a long time ago would have been great.

"We also had a fine swimming hole in the San Marcos River." Lily thought to herself that it was fun having Pappy-Gene visit them. It was making him happy to have someone to share memories with about long ago. Mother had told Lily that grandparents had a wealthy store of information and experiences. She said children could learn many things from them, as well as learn how to tell stories interestingly.

"There was a long chain with a big ring in it

NOTES

hanging from a limb over the river," said Pappy-Gene, demonstrating how to hold onto the ring.

"We did a lot of swimming to keep cool. The water in the river was from two to ten feet deep, clear and cold.

"The only drug store in town had an electric ceiling fan near the front door." Pappy-Gene held his hat between his thumb and pointing finger while he scratched his head with the other fingers on that hand, trying to recollect. He replaced his hat and said he thought the fan was mostly to keep the flies out, because there was no screen door.

"In the summertime the kids would congregate under the fan and Mr. King, the owner, would occasionally run us kids off so we wouldn't block the doorway. 'You kids run on off and play now. Get! Run on out of here so people can get in and out, you hear?' he would say to us."

Lily giggled at the thought of Pappy-Gene being young and getting scolded. She said, "Pappy-Gene, we have a ceiling fan in our living room. It

NOTES

does move the air around and make it cooler. What else, Pap?" Lily was really enjoying these adventures.

"Are you writing all this down, Lily? How are you going to remember all these stories?" asked Pappy-Gene.

Lily got her pencil and notebook out of her backpack and began writing. She could even put these in her journal. That would make her mother happy because she was always telling Lily it was a good idea to keep a journal of special things.

"What did Mamaw do to keep cool, Pap?"

"I've seen her a million times doing her work in the kitchen, with a wet washcloth on the back of her neck. She would rinse it out every once in a while when her neck warmed up the cloth. Fresh water would make it cool again. She would go red in the face and I thought she would pass out with the heat, but when she put the wet cloth on the back of her neck, she would sit down and rest and feel better."

Lily's grandmother had been dead two years

NOTES

but Lily remembered her lovingly.

Lily remembered that her grand-father had been a railroad engineer on the Texas and Pacific Railroad, and she asked, "What did you do on those hot old engines? Weren't they run by burning coal, Pap? Wasn't sitting by a big hot fire unbearable?" Lily's questions ran on.

Pappy-Gene said, "You said it, Lily. My, yes! Even the diesels, later on, were hot. But we railroaders wore overalls and a jumper. You know, the blue striped ones? With a matching cap? When the jumper got wet with perspiration it was cool, especially when the train was running down the railroad tracks and the breeze came through the cab. Did you know that God made each of us with our own personal-air conditioning, Lily?"

Lily's mouth fell open but nothing came out! Just questions were in her eyes. Pap could see the wheels in her mind turning trying to figure that out!

"Well, if you never perspired, you would die. What happens when we get too hot?"

NOTES

"We sweat--uh, perspire, like I did today."

"It is a good thing you did, Lily, 'cause when some air got to you, it cooled you off, didn't it? What did you feel when you rode your bike home from Primary?"

Lily's eyes lighted up, "Yeah! It was cooler when I was riding. I felt the breeze and it felt good--and when I sat down under the Million Dollar Tree, I hadn't dried off and I got cooler."

"That's because you stopped generating heat by moving around and peddling your bike. You sat still a few minutes and you cooled off some more, didn't you? Perspiring wets yourself and the air cools you down--there is your own air conditioning system--air and water!"

"Do you know, Lily, you can't drink ice cold water when you are really hot because you get cramps in your stomach? Did you ever get a bad bellyache from drinking cold water?"

Lily was trying to remember when Pappy-Gene went on with his story.

NOTES

"The railroad engines had water coolers on them and I would set the tin cup on the boiler for a minute to take the chill off of the water so I wouldn't get a bellyache."

Pappy-Gene smiled and wondered if he dared tell Lily what he remembered about the rest of the train story. He dared!

"On the railroad when we got to our destination, we had to spend the night and take another train back home the next day. So I climbed the stairs of the hotel where the railroaders stayed overnight, and sometimes, if the temperature reached one hundred, a little ten-inch fan was put in our rooms. That wasn't very much help, but I figured out a way to help cool off. I guess it was kind of a desperate thing to do, but before I went to bed, I'd pour a whole pitcher of water all over the bed and then jump in!"

Lily broke into squealing giggles.

Pappy-Gene continued, "I thought maybe I could get to sleep before it dried--but don't you try

NOTES

that!" Pappy-Gene warned, "Mattresses in our houses these days would be ruined with that much water!"

Lily rolled on the grass laughing. "Wait till my friend, Marjorie, hears this, Pappy! She'll die!" Lily laughed till tears came to her eyes.

Pappy grinned at this reaction, as he watched Lily out of the corner of his eye. She settled down in a minute and said, "Pappy-Gene, these are the best stories. I'm going to have a great report. I'll never complain about hot weather again! If I get too hot, I'll just get a wash cloth and wet it like Mamaw did when she was alive, and put it around the back of my neck."

"You wouldn't be afraid your friends would laugh at you about these stories?" asked Pappy-Gene.

"Not if the stories keep us from dying! I've heard about people getting heat strokes. Now I know why! They must have gotten too hot for their own air conditioners to work!" acknowledged Lily.

NOTES

"Or," Pappy suggested, "Just turn on the fan or air-conditioner in the house! You can count them as blessings any day."

"We surely can, but Pap, Lily turned onto her back on the cool grass and watched the high clouds moving across the sky through the peep holes in the sprawling branches of the Million-Dollar Tree. She had been reminded of many things to be thankful for in the hot summertime. Her Mom, Dad and brothers and sisters would love her report.

Maybe it would help when she got hot, just to think about swimming and eating ice cream, and playing in tunnels, or THINK about Pap pouring water on his bed to cool off before there was air conditioning!

NOTES

****

Suggested Exercise

Q. What things did Pappy-Gene do to keep cool that did not include the use of air and water? (Even the tunnel had cool air. Stayed in the shade, avoided exercise during the heat of the day.)

Q. How did people keep foods cool before there were refrigerators? (They lowered food to the water in wells, or put it in spring houses.)

Q. How does our personal-air conditioning work? (We drink plenty of water, perspire, and when the air hits us we cool off.)

Q. How would you tell if someone were sick from too much heat? (Their skin would be hot, red, and dry. Their sweating mechanism is blocked! They may pass out. This is life threatening. Get help quickly.)

Q. What first aid would you give them? (Cool them quickly: turn hose on them, cold tub (no ice), fan, air conditioned room. If temperature starts to rise again, repeat above.)

Q. If your friend turns pale, perspires LOTS, vomits, has leg and stomach cramps, headache, he may have heat exhaustion. What would you do for him? (Lay him down, put his feet up about a foot, loosen his clothing, cool him off with wet cloths and have him drink water with a little salt in it, unless he vomits. Tell him to rest and stay cool for a few days.)

Draw a picture about this story here, or to build comprehension, write your version of the story on this page.

Where several children are using one book, have them draw a picture or write their story and put their best work in their journals.

NOTES

TWO LITTLE GIRLS IN TEXAS

THE OLD ICE BOX

"Those children will drown, Pauline!" Mamaw called to her married daughter who had left her two little girls in a bubble bath in the tub. The squeals of laughter had silenced and Mamaw thought for sure something was wrong!

Pauline ran to check, just in case, but found the two piling bubbles high on their blond curly tops.

"It's time to get out, you two. Here, get these towels around your heads, and when I dry you off you can get your undies on and look out of the bedroom window at the rain."

NOTES

Bathing at Mamaw's house next door, was more fun any day than bathing at home. Their mother went for clean clothes while the children crawled up on the widow seat in the bedroom to wait for her.

Betty Gene, nicknamed Genie, was nearly three and her older sister by seventeen months, sat at the open window watching the warm summer rain drip from the roof top onto the clean white sand below the window. The sand was made earth colored by tiny rust specks in it.

"Sister", or Mattie Eula, was the firstborn and named for each of her grandmothers, but she became "Sister" to the whole family when Genie came along. Mattie Eula was quite a mouthful for little friends anyway, and their proper given names were used only when there mother, Pauline meant business!

"Sister, you can't eat the sand anymore." Genie was reading Sister's mind. "Mother said it would make your tummy hurt again."

NOTES

"I won't." Sister looked at the fine granules of sand. She did not know why she liked eating dirt or sand. She didn't even mind the grittiness. It was just something she did every chance she got, when the promise not to eat it was no longer fresh on her mind.

Being three and four and a half years old was quite marvelous when you lived next door to your grandmother and could go over just about every day if you wanted.

Mother came into the bedroom with clean underwear and clean, starched overalls over her arm. "Let's get those towels off your heads, and get you into your overalls. Come on. Genie, you first. Sister," Pauline handed a pair of the overalls to her, "you dress yourself. You're a big girl. I'll help Genie."

Mother unwrapped the towel from Genie's curly, blond hair and brushed it over her head to finish the drying, "You girls! Your hair is so kinky, I can't tell which end grows into your head. Wish I had curly hair like that." Mother often added, "Does no

NOTES

good to comb your hair, it jumps right back into curls the way it wants to anyhow." Mother patted each head with loving fondness and no little pride.

Their little blouses under the overalls matched, but there would be no shoes today. The spring rain had cooled things off, and the Texas sun, now peeking around the passing clouds, would dry the sidewalk and grass shortly, and the children needed to go outside and play and not be under Mamaw's and Pauline's busy feet today.

"Our overalls are brand new! Mamaw," Sister called out to their grandmother, "Look, we look like Daddy!"

Betty Gene and Sister looked at their new, but scratchy overalls that were navy blue with white pin stripes up and down just like the railroad men wore. Their father was a railroad engineer and the girls were impressed. Running big locomotives was exciting, especially when he let you ride up in the cab with him in the switch yard and pull down on the cord that made a loud, long whistle blow.

NOTES

Sister asked, "Where are our soft ones, Mother?"

"Sister, you kids have completely worn out the seats on your others. I keep telling you not to slide down those concrete banisters while you wait for the ice man. Just sit on the steps, do you hear? These overalls have to last you a long time."

It was important to conserve as much as possible. Railroaders did not make a lot of money, and the big depression was growing deeper and more oppressive every day.

Mamaw warned, "If you promise just to sit still and watch for the ice man to come down the street, I'll let you turn the card in the window so he will know how much ice to bring in."

Mamaw had taught Sister how to read the numbers on the four sides of the card, and learning anything new was exciting to Sister, especially when Mamaw did the teaching.

Sister picked up the card and demonstrated that she knew the numbers, "See, this says ten, for

NOTES

ten pounds," then turning the card a bit, she continued, "This says twenty five, this says fifty, and the one with the zeros says one hundred."

"That's right, Sister. You remember well. Now, whose birthday is it tomorrow?" asked Mamaw.

"Genie's," and simultaneously Genie chimed in, "Mine!"

"And what do we do when we have birthdays?" asked Mother.

"Make ice cream!" The girls jumped up and down and clapped their hands together.

Sister asked, "Mamaw, how much ice do we need to make ice cream?"

"Well, the ice man only comes twice a week, so we will have to order seventy-five pounds. The old ice box will hold only fifty, but we'll wrap the other piece of ice in tow sacks and put it in the shade so it won't melt too fast," answered Mamaw.

"Now, you children run on out and watch for him while your mother and I get the corn bottled. Run along."

NOTES

Mamaw turned to Mother, the oldest of her seven children, and reminded her that her younger brothers alone could put away nearly a freezer full of ice cream in one afternoon, so they would need plenty.

Sister put the card in the living room window with the seventy-five number at the top, and the girls went outside on the front porch which ran the length of the West Seventh Street house. They climbed into the front porch swing which hung by chains from the porch ceiling and began swinging and singing Bye Bye Blackbird.

Immediately they heard their Mother say in an excited voice, "Oh, Mama, I got so busy with the children's bath I forgot to empty the dripper pan. Look, it is all over the porch floor!"

Pauline cautioned her mother, "Mama, don't slip in the water and fall!"

The back porch had been screened in to make another room, and there the long kitchen table accommodated the large family still at home. There

NOTES

also was the large ice box to prevent the ice man from having to drip melting ice across floors in the house.

Mamaw had her hands full of ears of corn, but stopped and put them on the chair before entering the room.

The children ran to the screen door and pressed their faces against the screen so hard it made patches on their noses. They looked, but dared not go in and get in the way of the disaster.

"Pauline, the mop is on the back porch. You get that and I'll empty the rest of the water in the dripper," Mamaw tiptoed through the water on the floor, lifted her skirts into a roll above her knees, leaned over and gently pulled the dripper pan out from under the wooden ice box, spilling the over-running pan of water even more.

Pauline mopped and mopped and every few minutes had to wring the water out of the rag mop into a bucket so it could be thrown out into the back yard under the hackberry tree.

NOTES

"Keep the mop handy, Pauline, we will have to mop up later. The ice man is sure to track in mud after that shower today."

The ice was always placed into a tin box in the upper chamber of the wooden chest and all members of the family knew not to lift the lid anymore than was absolutely necessary because that would hasten the melting. That caused the water to drip too fast down the inside pipe at the rear of the ice box to the pan on the floor beneath. Beside that, maintaining coldness would keep the food fresh longer in the bottom half of the ice box.

A door on the front of the wooden ice box gave access to two shelves that held food, and you could see the drip pipe in one corner, on its way down to the drip pan. The tin walls of the ice box were usually wet with moisture and had to be wiped away with hot, soda water, rinsed and dried every week.

The children looked through the screen door, and down through the hallway to see and hear bits of the activity going on.

NOTES

Sister told Genie, "Two times a day you have to empty the drip pan, and put it back under the ice box."

Spellbound and wide-eyed, Genie agreed, "Yeah."

Once Sister wanted to empty the dripper pan Pauline said, "It's messy to empty. You have to carefully pull the pan out, then carry it to the sink, and pour it out without spilling it! Have you ever tried to carry a long, shallow pan full of water very far?" Mother knew Sister had not.

Sister shook her head, then remembered, "I tried to carry water to the dog in a shallow pan. It spilled all over me! I had to get a bucket to water the dog." She added, "He didn't mind. He just licked my hands and legs and got it all off."

Pauline rolled her eyes toward the ceiling and shook her head, "Mercy, mercy! Do they ever learn about germs and animals, Mama?"

Seeing that Mamaw and their mother had things under control, the girls went to the five steps

NOTES

at the end of the front walk to watch for the ice man. On each side of the concrete steps were banisters that made the greatest slides, however slow, because they were not as slippery as the metal ones at the school yard where a person could go lickety split down to the ground. Having just been warned not to wear out their new overalls, the girls sat on the steps for the long wait.

Watching for the ice man was one ritual Genie and Sister loved. "It takes the ice man so long to get here." But once spotted, Sister stood up, danced up and down and called to Genie, "Look, I can see Ole Jack! He is coming around the corner." Genie mimicked Sister's every move.

Just as suddenly, the dancing took on another meaning, "Uh-oh, I have to go pivy, Sister," said Genie. "Let's hurry quick."

The path, lined by weeds and tall grass, led to the outhouse at the back of the wash shed. A small tree grew beside it and gave a little shade for the occupants on hot summer days. A diamond shaped

NOTES

hole was cut in the side wall, up high, for light and ventilation and a half moon hole was cut in the door. There was a loop of leather to pull the door open which had sprung hinges on it. After you went inside, you had to turn a small piece of wood, swiveling on a nail, across the door so no one else could come in while it was in use.

A Sears and Roebuck catalog hung on a wire. If you used just one black and white or yellow page and scrubbed it between your hands for a minute the paper would soften and not be so scratchy to use. The colored pages were too stiff and better for looking at the pictures while "concentrating"!

It took both the children to reach things and care for each other when trips to the privy were made. Some times while you sat on the long wooden, two holed seat, you could see big spiders in the corners of the out-house, spinning their webs in which to catch flies. Below the Sears and Roebuck catalog a shovel and a bucket of white lime stood in the corner. After using the privy you sprinkled a

NOTES

shovelful of lime down the holes.

"Why?" asked Genie.

"Aunt Marguerite said it was to keep the paper from the catalog from catching on fire--here, let me do that, Genie, you'll drop the shovel in the hole, then mother will say mercy, mercy to us."

Sister took Genie by the hand and they hurried back to the front steps, to wait for Dan the ice man and Ole Jack, his remarkable horse. Genie pulled her bloomers up with one hand as they hurried along.

They watched Dan, the driver, step down off the back end of the ice wagon and pick up a block of ice with big heavy tongs, and deliver it through the back door of a house down the street. Then after what seemed an eternity, he jumped back onto the step at the back of the wagon and called to Ole Jack, "Geddiup, Jack...Geeee."

That meant for Ole Jack to go across the street to the next house with a card in the window. When Dan wanted Ole Jack to cross back to the other side

NOTES

again he would say, "Gettiup, Jack. C'mon, hawww, Jack, hawww."

Dan seldom needed the reins which ran from the horse along the inside of the covered wagon through a long window slit in the front wall. Big hooks held the reins near the back step.

"Ole Jack sure is smart, Genie," marveled Sister as she took all this in.

Once Sister, who loved to learn things, had watched other men drive buggies or wagons from a seat up on the front end of a wagon. She wondered why Dan stood on the back step of the wagon all the time, but she listened as the wagon rattled and the horse clopped on down the street.

"Won't Ole Jack turn down the wrong street or miss somebody's house?" She had asked of Mamaw who had all the answers.

"Oh, no. Dan has taught Ole Jack just what to do. He has delivered ice for so many years he knows that when Dan says "Geeee" he needs to go to the right side of the street, and when Dan says, "Gettiup,

NOTES

Hawww", he is supposed to go left. And Dan always stops in front of every house he comes to unless he sees the blank side of the card in the window."

"Then what happens, Mamaw?" asked Sister.

"Then Dan tells Jack to gettiup again."

Genie was getting excited and impatient for the ice man to chip away the amount of ice needed and deliver it into house after house. The girls watched water dripping from the ice wagon leaving a trail on the drying dirt road and sometimes splashing into the few puddles left from the rain.

So impatient were they that Genie forgot the promise not to slide down the concrete banister and away she went. Sister joined her by climbing to her side of the steps and slid down.

Soon Genie was saying, "One more house! I hope he hasn't given away all the chips," because all along the street other children waited for the ice man too.

Dan knew most children by their first names and well he knew why they waited for him.

NOTES

The children as well were familiar with the tall broad shouldered man who wore a big flat piece of leather over one shoulder so he could swing the large pieces of ice onto his back for carrying. Dan said he didn't mind the wet dripping down him in the hot summer, but the cold ice tightened up his back muscles and made it difficult to lift and carry the big blocks all day long. The thick leather piece protected Dan's back.

Sometimes Dan took his sharp ice pick out of the leather holster hanging low from his belt and he chipped through the large blocks of ice leaving several slivers of ice scattered around. After having used the ice pick sometimes he just stuck it into the wooden floor of the wagon.

The ice chips fell onto the tow sacks placed on the floor of the wagon to keep the ice from sliding out the back when Ole Jack jerked the wagon into a roll.

Children danced on their toes to look over the heads of those in front of them and held their hands

NOTES

together, waiting for icy tokens from Dan. Dan always obliged, and patiently passed out the treats no matter how small a chip could be found.

"Oooh, it's cold. Lick it fast, 'fore it melts," cried the children, who ran to their sidewalks or lawns to put the ice down quickly.

Mamaw once observed that somehow none of the children were ever heard to complain about who got the largest piece of ice!

"Well, there's Genie and Sister this morning. What are you two doing out here so early?" asked Dan, knowing full well why they waited.

"Could we please have some ice, please, Mister Dan?" they asked, being sure to say please.

"Looks like it's all gone, girls," teased Dan.

Dropped faces suddenly began to smile because Sister and Genie knew he would chip off small pieces for them even if there weren't any left from the other choppings.

Dan chopped a fifty pound piece and a smaller twenty-five pound block of ice for Mamaw's ice box,

NOTES

but before taking them one at a time into the house by the back door, Dan handed each of the girls slivers of transparent, watery, drippy, cold, cold ice. Wonderful ice for hot summer days in Texas made life worth living!

"Oh, thank you, thank you," they said as they hurriedly returned to the sidewalk.

"It freezes my hands, Sister. It's too cold!" cried Genie.

"I know. Bite it off, and make a river with the rest on the sidewalk. See?" Sister began writing the ice card numbers on the hot concrete, and watched the riverlets run away from the numerals.

Before the ice completely melted, Sister sat on the bottom end of the banister, lay back so her back fitted into the warm curve, and licked away at the icy treat in her dribbling, icy blue fingers. Life was cruelly sweet on the hot summer day.

"Birthdays are wonderful when you are young. Birthdays are wonderful when you are old, but somehow less celebrated," Mother reckoned.

NOTES

Mother sat a little more often this summer. Sister and Genie were going to have a little brother or sister in about three months, and it was nice living next door so Mother's sisters could help with things like parties. However there would be the family at the party and the little girl across the street to come and help celebrate.

Of Mamaw's big family of boys and girls, only Uncle Raymond was the right age to direct the ice cream freezing. After the aunts, Louise, Ivalee and Marguerite made the custard vanilla ice cream, it was poured into the freezer, and the lid was put on and fitted to the hand crank apparatus.

Now it was time to freeze the ice cream for the party. Raymond filled the space between the milk container and the wooden bucket with layers of ice and salt.

"Don't let that salt water get into the ice cream, Raymond," called Pauline.

"I won't, but you gotta put enough salt in it to make the ice melt or else it won't freeze anything!"

NOTES

Raymond answered. He had done this before. Then he took a tow sack, folded it just so and placed it on top of the freezer.

"Who's going to sit on the tow sack first?" Raymond reached over and got Genie and put her on top of the gunny sack. Then he turned the crank and the girls began to squeal!

What a funny sight to see Genie being wiggled. Her curls bounced and her cheeks and chin jiggled, and the freezer made noise over their squeals.

Footnote:

How can young aunts explain the indelicate subject of caring for out door toilets to forever questioning children? Powdered lime was the only sanitation measure known before flushing toilets! One-half of one "hand shovel "full of lime, sprinkled down the holes following use, kept down moisture, odor, and the multiplication of flies!

****

Suggested Exercise

1. Why was Mattie Eula called "Sister"?
2. Where do you suppose dripper cake pans may have gotten their names?
3. How did the ice man know how much ice to deliver to each house?
4. Where do you get your ice cream?

Have you ever made or eaten snow ice cream? (3 eggs, 2 ts vanilla, 3/4 c sugar or honey, mix well in 1 cup milk, add to a big pan of clean snow! Devour immediately!)

5. What did Pauline say to the children when they did perplexing things? Why? (She was asking Heavenly Father to help her have patience with two growing children!)

Draw a picture about this story here, or to build comprehension, write your version of the story on this page.

Where several children are using one book, have them draw a picture or write their story and put their best work in their journals.

NOTES

THE BEAUTY CONTEST

Life in Bonham, in northeast Texas, in the mid 1920s was quite eventful when you considered that Saturday matinees were overcrowded with children who came to see the next episode of Hopalong Cassidy and Mickey Mouse. Once a year the local theater was used for other grand productions, such as the Fannin County Baby Beauty Contests.

Aunt Marguerite, and Aunt Ivalee especially took over the task of making this contest competitive. They had two small, curly haired blond nieces so much the same size they might pass for twins!

Dressing them alike would do the trick! Aunt Louise had a knack for sewing, so out came the scissors and measuring tape. It had to be done in

NOTES

blue and white satin, with their names across their tummies from one shoulder to their hips. Oh! And makeup must be applied just perfectly--not too much.

"Be still, Betty Gene. Oh, this lipstick is too dark! It must be bright pink."

Everyone's purse was gone through to come up with the perfect combination. Short golden hair was ribboned and black patent leather shoes with white anklets and a white handkerchief tucked under a blue wrist ribbon would do the trick.

There are two versions about what happened next! One says that the twin blondies won a Blue Ribbon or at least the Sweepstakes with hands down! It must have been that Aunts would take no other outcome and made the younger of the two believe they won in spite of the judgments.

But since the tale teller is older and remembers first hand, the following version simply must be the correct one! It went like this:

The stage was so big, the audience so

NOTES

immense and noisy that Sister and Genie were petrified. This wasn't the way they thought it would be at all. Genie could hardly be persuaded to go on stage, to follow dimpled darlings with dazzling costumes and confidence. The great applause was entirely too frightening! Maybe if she held Sister's hand it would work!

Finally peeking around Sister's hindside, the two sort of skinny, satin-bedecked kinky-haired blondes timidly brought their wide eyes and no smiles onto the stage. From off stage Aunt Marguerite and Aunt Ivalee loudly whispered directions and encouragement. Sister tripped and nearly fell over Genie, they both looked back to their coaches, paused momentarily and ran hurriedly offstage to the other side!

No, they didn't win-except with their Mother, Grandmother and aunties, but I guess memories do belong to the rememberer.

NOTES

****

Suggested Exercise

Q. Are you shy about giving talks or singing before others?

Q. Are you especially good at drawing or playing ball or fixing things?

Q. What do you think would make it easier for you to give a short talk all by yourself?

Q. Would you think about this carefully and choose someone to talk with about your ideas?

Q. In order to tell others about the gospel being on the earth now, it is a good idea to learn not to be afraid to give talks. Would you like to be able to do this easily?

Q. Heavenly Father is the best person to ask for help. He may show you in a dream some night how to overcome shyness. Will you ask him to help you?

Draw a picture about this story here, or to build comprehension, write your version of the story on this page.

Where several children are using one book, have them draw a picture or write their story and put their best work in their journals.

NOTES

CHRISTMAS ON NEVER DONE FARM

It was a rainy, cold day in November. This kind of day beckoned Martha to curl up on the couch with a good book and a crisp apple. But she finished putting away the utensils and listened to grandmother's steps, back and forth, as she carried the last of her berry jam into the pantry. Grandmother came into the large sitting room to her loom, sat with her back to the fire and took a deep breath of satisfaction.

Martha knew Grandmother's next move. It would be to give a sigh of relief to be off her feet! Then she watched Grandmother pick up the threads and shuttle and resume weaving the toweling she had begun weeks ago.

NOTES

The rain had turned to snow and Old Henry, the cat, back from the barn with a stomach full of mice, could feel that winter was on its way. He circled a favorite spot on the braided rug in front of the fireplace and settled down to absorb the warmth of the hearth. The click of the shuttle and the bump of the warp would not interrupt Henry's purr, nor would the sound of Martha's voice as she read to Grandmother. It was fun coming to Grandmother's house.

But today instead of reading, Martha wanted to hear about the early days on Never Done Farm in Kentucky where Grandmother grew up. Since Martha was the only one who seemed genuinely interested, and since Grandmother dearly loved being cajoled into reminiscing, this seemed to be the perfect day to have her re-live her childhood days.

"Grandmother, please tell me about your favorite Christmas again, the one on 'Never Done Farm'."

Grandma knew Martha loved her stories so

NOTES

she obliged.

"Oh, we had wonderful times when I was a girl. Not much time for play, but the twins, Cornelia and Cordelia, and I used to have our mother tell about her own mother's favorite Christmas, two generations back! Would you like to hear about that?"

"Hummmm, two generations back from you--that would be four generations from me. Did she live on Never Done Farm, too?"

"Sure did. Grandmother Evelyn--your great-great-grandmother--was a Whitlow before she married Grandpa Pedigo. Louis T. was his name."

Martha had that feeling again. Grandmother was about to unravel one of her wonderful stories. Funny thing was, they were all true, and that's what made them wonderful.

Grandmother began her story from the beginning:

"There was great excitement back in the hills and "hollers" of the Great White Smokey Mountains

NOTES

in Kentucky. It was December of 1848 and my mother, Evelyn Whitlow, was having an important and unusual Christmas!

"Unusual because Evelyn was 'promised' to Louis T. Pedigo, a handsome young man who lived not far away and owned a lot of timber land. They were to be married a few days before Christmas and Christmases were already filled with family socials, and small get together where planning with unselfishness and sacrifices promised to make the spirit of giving genuine.

"What sacrifices, Grandmother?" asked Martha.

Grandmother replied, "Most pioneer families were poor. Typical gifts were ones of practicality if the families were poor. Small children found dolls made of stockings stuffed with cotton, or hand carved wooden toys. The teenage children got an orange stuck full of whole cloves and tied with bright pieces of yarn to be placed in dresser drawers for their fragrance."

NOTES

Grandma paused, sniffed in the air and said, "Ummmm, I can smell them still. So fragrant. The whole house had that sweet cinnamon and fruit aroma, Ummmm."

Martha smiled at Grandmother's dramatics.

"There were usually many children in families and personal things and pleasures had to be given up or shared to make Christmas nice for someone else! And neighbors and relatives from everywhere gathered around. Celebrations included "Singings" and candy pulling, sleigh-rides and hog killing in anticipation of side bacon, hams and sausage for the holidays and thereafter.

"This special Christmas Evelyn's father gave her a little shiny black mare, which is comparable to the gift of an automobile these days! After all, transportation then was by horses, wagons, buggies or on foot!

"Evelyn loved the beautiful black mare. Besides, the mare added to her dowry. Evelyn had saved for two unbleached muslin sheets, had

NOTES

embroidered and hemmed four bleached flour sacks for pillow cases. She had even crocheted a white border to the hems. My, they looked pretty!

"She had carefully picked the seams of six flour sacks which she then washed and allowed to blow in the sunshine and wind to make them soft and white for her hope chest. They made lovely dish cloths. Of course she saved the string she had picked from the flour sack seams. You didn't throw away anything in those days."

"Grandmother, I've seen your dish cloths made out of flour sacks. I use them when I dry your dishes." Martha had asked about the purple grapes embroidered on Grandmother's dish cloths one time.

"Sheets, pillow cases for the goose down pillows, and dish cloths and quilts were important items for any girl's dowry. Property or animals also helped the couple to get a good start. That is what dowries are for, Martha, to help a couple get a reasonable start when they get married.

"My mom wants me to work on my hope chest

NOTES

things every winter when it is too cold outside to play. Is that my dowry, Grandmother?"

Grandmother nodded. "I should say so!" She continued her story. "Evelyn married Louis T. who had said, 'Come with me to Never Done Farm in Good Luck where my saw mill is set up. We have a warm barn where we can keep the mare.' Good Luck was a nearby community of friendly folks.

"Evelyn curried and tended the young mare with love and gentleness, even after their children began to come along--and come along they did, all eight of them!

"Evelyn and Louis T. were very happy because they knew how to work and to love doing it. And though the children came along pretty fast, Louis T. was kind and helpful. He taught the children that it was important to work. There were so few time saving and work saving appliances in those days. Everybody had to work to get along."

"Grandmother, I only like to work when someone else is working with me." Martha wrinkled

NOTES

up her nose at the thought of work.

"Why Martha, you did a splendid job bringing in the wood from the wood pile last night all by yourself."

"Grandpa Louis T. used to say, 'Working teaches that if you do it honestly you get the desired results; if you slack off or put off work in the garden it produces mostly weeds that smother the food and makes it harder to come by. And if you work in the saw mills honestly and carefully, your machinery doesn't break down as often, your hired people respect you and are faithful to get to work on time and to be responsible.'

"Louis T. always said, 'It feels good to know people can count on you. It feels good to know you can count on the Lord.'

"Grandmother, you keep talking about good feelings inside you. I've watched and I am beginning to catch those good feelings happening inside me. I felt good today when you said you would tell me stories, real stories about real people. I also felt

NOTES

good feelings when I worked hard on my mathematics the best I could, and sure enough the problems turned out all right!"

"Martha, those good feelings are the ones you get over some honest or kind thing you have done or someone has done to you. Have you found that to be true?"

Martha was thinking that idea over when Grandmother continued.

"But in spite of hard work and good intentions, Louis T. also always said, 'Life is life and there are blessed growing experiences for everyone.'

"Tragedy struck just a couple of months before the Civil War broke out!"

Martha interrupted, "Uh oh, here come some blessed growing experiences!"

"You are right, Martha, Louis T. had to go nine miles away into Summer Shade--" Grandmother interrupted herself, "Isn't that a beautiful name for a town? Summer Shade." Grandmother let the name roll off her tongue as she pictured it in her mind.

NOTES

Grandmother always noticed things like that.

"But Granpa Louis T. had to go to Summer Shade on business and cautioned Evelyn about the guerrillas who often came from Tennessee to steal horses and cattle in preparation for the war.

"He had not been gone long when several men rode up the lane to their home looking for horses! Louis T. had taken the plow horses with the wagon, but the mare was there in the barn!

"Evelyn, pregnant and in her seventh month with her fifth baby, hurried out and took the mare by her bridle and would not let her go. The men whipped Evelyn unmercifully with their quirts, but she would not let go of the mare. Finally they rode off without her.

"When Louis T. returned, saw Evelyn's deep, open wounds from the leather quirts and heard the story, he was terribly upset and concerned about her and her unborn child. He couldn't understand how people who called themselves men could mistreat a woman! Particularly one who could do them no

NOTES

harm! However, the next day Louis T. had to finish his business in Summer Shade and said, 'I will take the mare with me in case the guerrillas come back for her.'

"'Oh, no! You might meet them on the road and they will take her from you,' cried Evelyn.

"'Now, my dear, how could they take from a man what they couldn't take from a woman?' Louis T. replied reassuringly.

"But sure enough, Louis T. met the band of guerrillas and they boldly spoke up to him, demanding the horse.

"'We felt sorry for your wife, but we will shoot you without hesitation!' He had to let them take the horse.

"Oh, Grandmother. How awful!" Martha was saddened.

"Louis T. walked back home feeling as mournful as he knew Evelyn would. He grieved sincerely for the loss and especially for Evelyn's disappointment. He promised himself, 'I must do

NOTES

something to make up for this terrible loss to Evelyn.'

Grandmother sent her shuttle speedily through the loom threads, looked with pride at the pattern developing on her loom, and continued.

"Evelyn gave an early birth to her baby, due to the harsh treatment of the guerrillas. But he was strong, healthy and they named him--get this, Martha, do you remember our talking about Uncle Pouncie Nuckols Pedigo? That was Uncle Pouncie!"

They laughed. Martha had indeed grown up hearing Uncle Pouncie's name. Martha's aunts and uncles used to laugh and repeat what Uncle Pouncie's wife, Nancy Ophelia, said when they came to dinner. She was a tiny mite of a lady, and he was a tall robust man, and heavy set. She didn't eat very much and would always ask, 'Pouncie, want my meat?'"

The family, of strictest table manners, would grin but quickly wipe the smiles away at this little scene.

Hearing about Pouncie's birth into this world

NOTES

was an added pleasure for Martha.

"A few years after the war Louis T. built a little axe-hewn, notched-cornered log cabin church just a hundred yards from the house. He went to Tennessee and got a preacher to service the small community of Predestinarian, "Hardshell" Primitive Baptists.

"'I'm deeding the church house and the property it stands on to the members so you, my wife, won't have so far to go to get religion and we can bring up the children right.'"

"By the time people began to enjoy the new church another Christmas was nearing and there was a problem!"

"What problem, Grandmother?" Martha was curious again.

"Well, when people came from home in the cold wintry weather all bundled in wagons or buggies with hearth stones at their feet, or on horses, then sat by the pot bellied stove in the church house, they would get toasty warm and doze off!

NOTES

"The Elders were so proud of the new church they figured out a way to keep everyone awake during the sermons!

"What would they do?' Martha wondered.

"'Well, two long poles were prepared with a feather and a soft rubber ball tied to the ends. The designated person would tickle the noses of the women with the feather and bounce the ball off the heads of the gentlemen if they fell asleep!'

"The children, wide eyed with amazement, laughed but didn't dare complain."

Martha was not sure she believed what she had heard. "Ahh, Grandmother, would they really do that to people?"

Grandmother stopped her weaving and peered at Martha over the rims of her glasses and asked, "Would *you* go to sleep if you knew someone in the corner was reaching for a pole?"

Chagrinned, Martha leaned back on the couch not sure she would not have fallen asleep herself if she had been there.

NOTES

"Grandpa Louis T. was quiet, kind and well respected in the community. He was very well read of the scriptures. He knew them so well that if the minister misquoted one in his sermon, it is said that Louis T. would stand straight up and kindly say, 'Reverend, I believe that goes...' and he would recite the whole verse without missing a word, then sit down.

Martha chuckled again as she reflected upon grandmother's wonderful stories of Christmas and life on 'Never Done' Farm long ago.

She thought about many things. Things like heated or cooled, wind, sun or rain-free automobiles that are so comfortable. There was instant communication with the rest of the world. Cars that could quickly whisk her away to anywhere. She thought about other blessings such as hot running water, peaceful valleys, an air-conditioned, or well-heated, comfortable church just up the street. The hard work sometimes grouched about needed to be appreciated.

NOTES

She thought about Christmases that come and go, bringing the same kind of snow that fell on 'Never Done' Farm in Kentucky. Martha thought she could even smell the pine needles and turkey dinners, the aroma of oranges pricked by whole cloves and hung with bright yarn to add a festive air. She could just see baskets of nuts that had been gathered on the farm, pecan and pumpkin pies, and pine cones snuggled here and there among the boughs along the tall, hand carved fireplace front and the mantel.

It was easy to compare colorful packages under trees that had been purchased in parking lots on winter days. She thought about how they added to Christmases that were special--but no more special than those spent in yesteryears on Never Done Farm in Kentucky. Yes, her second great-grandma Evelyn and Grandpa Louis T. Pedigo and their eight children had cut their own trees from their own land and gave each other hand-knitted mittens, woolen stockings, and little black mares for Christmas.

NOTES

****

Suggested Exercise

Q. Have you tapped your grandparents' store of wonderful stories? Each family member tell his favorite story to the rest of the class.

A. If you do not have a grandparent who can tell you stories, or write them to you, have one or both of your parents tell favorite stories of their own grandparents.

A. If there is a widow or widower living in your community, one of the kindest things you can do to make them still feel needed is to sit at their feet and learn. They may have wonderful stories to tell.

Q. Each family member may want to tell their favorite family Christmas traditions. Is there a special one you would like to add to your list this year?

Q. Which tradition from Never Done Farm do you like best?

Draw a picture about this story here, or to build comprehension, write your version of the story on this page.

Where several children are using one book, have them draw a picture or write their story and put their best work in their journals.

NOTES

LIVING THROUGH A HURRICANE

"What is it like to live through a hurricane?" Aunt Jane had come to spend Thanksgiving with the Webb relatives on the Gulf Coast of Texas. She knew that her nephew and his family could give a first hand report since their experience with a hurricane that had hit land in South Texas sometime before.

The Webbs lived just six miles inland where tropical storms and hurricanes were just part of life during certain months of the year.

Karen and Suzanne, eleven and nine at the time, remembered vividly when Tropical Storm Elisha was fast becoming a major hurricane in the Gulf of Mexico in 1982. The anxiety, the indecision of

NOTES

whether to leave and when, the tension all added to the worry about family irreplaceables that must be left behind when evacuating. Other considerations could only be understood by those who live in hurricane paths along coastlines.

Danbury, a small riceland farming community, about twenty miles west by northwest of Galveston Island was only ten feet above sea level.

Their father, Raymond Webb, and their mother, Kay, explained the circumstances.

"Aunt Jane, Brazoria County, Texas, often gets tropical storms of one size or another. Coping with high waters, alligators, millions of cottonmouth water moccasins, rattlers and mosquitoes is not unusual for us."

When she asked how they handled such things, Karen said, "We mow our grass often so we can see the snakes before they see us, hopefully!

Suzanne interrupted, "And carry flash lights after dark so we don't step on a snake!"

Ray explained that cottonmouths are more

NOTES

aggressive than other snakes. "They usually will not move when they hear or see you coming. They will just attack, and at times will chase you and bite."

Karen resumed her part of the story, "And we don't wade, or swim in the canals, or ditches or rice fields."

Again Suzanne added, "When we go swimming or picnicking along the Gulf, we don't go to the bathroom in the tall salt grass where the rattle snakes live! That is their habitat. We just use common sense. We get along fine."

Karen laughed, "One day two teenage boys came home with three tow sacks full of snakes they had shot in a rice field. Snake hunting is one of their favorite past times." The girls and their dad grinned at the shocked expression on Aunt Jane's face and watched her frame shiver at the mention of such things.

Concerned about Aunt Jane's hearing all the scary things, their mother, Kay, became the public relations advocate.

NOTES

"We have great scenery here. We see ships from all over the world and have everything anyone else has access to, and we have help when the hurricanes come. We listen to the National Weather Service. You know, the Hurricane Tracking Center broadcasts from Miami, Florida?" Kay ended her sentence with a questioning raise of the voice as Texans often do.

Aunt Jane had heard the weather service warnings on the radio and television even in northwest Texas.

"When a storm is brewing in the Gulf of Mexico, we go to my brother's ranch about ninety miles north of here. The relatives from this area take shelter there during hurricane seasons. Sometimes we use it as much as four times a year," Kay added.

"How fascinating! You seem to have this business of emergencies all worked out. But how do you know whether to stay or to evacuate in order to be safe?" Aunt Jane asked.

"The broadcasts let us know. But you see, that

NOTES

fall the weather service said that Elisha seemed to be headed south and west of Brazoria County. But we made traditional precautions just in case Elisha turned on us."

Ray remembered the details, "We bolted plywood over all the windows, put away any outside furniture that might blow away, and parked the cars in the barn with the tractor and truck. We also saw that fresh batteries for the portable TV, radio, and flashlights were in good supply, and checked to be sure extra food stuffs were in store for a three week period."

"Why three weeks?" Aunt Jane questioned.

Ray explained, "If hurricanes develop into Force Two or Force Three strengths, or more, power lines and telephones may be blown down and out of service for ten days to two weeks at least."

"Do you just sit around and worry?" Aunt Jane thought she would have done that.

"No, after we get everything ready, the family resumes life as usual. We go to work and about our

NOTES

business unless, or until we are warned to leave."

"When tropical storms reach a seventy-four miles per hour force, they constitute a hurricane, and the National Weather Service issues a hurricane WATCH. From then on people check their TVs or radios for hourly updates."

Everybody's eyes and ears were glued to Ray as he told his story.

"As the hurricane approaches our vicinity the Weather Service issues a hurricane WARNING for our area. Then it is time to be gone in a hurry, if not sooner!" said Karen's father. "It is critical that you time your evacuation not to be caught with thousands of other vehicles on the highways and byways when the hurricane hits," warned Kay.

The children filled in, "If that happens then everyone could get stranded and caught in the middle of the winds. They can turn your car over or sweep it away in the flood waters brought in from the Gulf!"

"The children warned us, 'We should get in the

NOTES

car right now and leave!'" said their mother who came into the room with a cool glass of punch for everyone.

"It is always fun going to the ranch for a few days. Nothing but mattresses are kept in walk-in closets and when everyone gathers, out they come! Beds are made on two large family room floors. Three bathrooms and three bedrooms accommodate everyone, and the kitchen is big enough to make do for all. We bring our own supplies and linens."

"On with the story," Ray said, "But by 5:00 p.m. Elisha had only reached eighty-five miles an hour and was one hundred-twenty five miles away from us. No worry," Ray justified.

"We have lived in this area several years and were used to gulf storms and I was sure that everything was under control. We were prepared. Elisha was headed away from us, so we decided we did not need to evacuate. We would just keep ourselves posted."

"However," Ray went on, "Soon we heard that

NOTES

thousands were crowding the highways getting away from the coast and Galveston Island. The island is connected to the mainland only by a causeway, and a railroad track, and a sea wall that helped break the force of such storms. By 9:00 p.m. Hurricane Elisha turned and headed straight for us!"

Aunt Jane was wide eyed and all ears! She rubbed her arms as if her skin had begun to crawl with apprehension.

Kay smiled and said, "We looked at each other and said, 'We should have left!'" Everyone laughed. It was easy to laugh, now that the hurricane was over.

"Elisha's winds were advanced to one hundred miles per hour and it was dark, the roads were jammed. We decided that to be caught out on the highway and be stranded for hours or days would be worse than staying, so the decision was made to stay home and make the best of it."

"Kay told me, 'Indecision is dangerous. He who hesitates is lost!'" Ray confessed. "I tried to be calm

NOTES

by telling myself that I had taken several major precautions when I built this brick home about six years before. Because we've often experienced high tides and swollen streams with rain storms, etc. I had built the house on a fifteen foot mound of dirt, anchored with thirty-two concrete piers, and so far we have never been flooded or washed out. That was in our favor."

What an education Aunt Jane was getting! It was scary, but captivating to listen to someone who had gone through this kind of experience.

"Hurricanes are measured by their intensity and wind velocity from 1-to-5. At Force 5, or two hundred miles per hour, they destroy everything in their paths! Elisha's force was now reaching an early Force 3, and still headed directly toward us," said Karen, who had become knowledgeable about hurricanes in school and by watching the Weather Service pre-storm briefings each year.

"Karen and Suzanne had been listening to broadcasts and watching TV updates about Elisha

NOTES

for six to eight hours and were tired and worn out. So we put them in the bedroom the farthest from the Gulf and after a few more prayers, they fell asleep," Kay explained.

"The portable radio reported, 'Freeport--the only deep water access port along the Texas coastline and just six miles from our house--has lost its power!'"

"Kay exclaimed, 'Oh no, we're next!' And immediately our power went out!" Ray recounted.

"It was 12:04 a.m. The wind was 105 mph and Elisha was about 50 miles away and bearing down on us," Kay remembered well.

"The weariness of the constant roar of the wind continued to make it difficult for us to hear each other speak. It sounded as if a locomotive were about to hit us, never doing so, but close enough to keep us under tremendous pressure for so long a time," said Ray.

"The rain poured so ferociously against the house we soon discovered that it was being forced

NOTES

through cracks around the windows. This was in spite of the fact that they had been tightly built and covered now with plywood. We stuffed towels along all the window sills and doors to soak up the water. We put the washer and dryer against the back door, secured under the door knob to keep the door from blowing open, even though it was locked."

Aunt Jane sat back in her seat trying to relax some of the tension that kept building! "This is frightening," she said. "Much more exciting than any movie I ever saw!"

Ray was caught up in the retelling and continued this very true tale. "At 2:50 a.m. the TV broadcasted a false report--unintentionally. Kay came to the bedroom where I was checking on the girls and said, 'Ray, they just said that the top two floors of the Hotel Galvez are gone!'"

Hotel Galvez on Galveston Island was about eight stories high, was a heavy stone building that had withstood many storms over the years.

Aunt Jane gasped, "Oh, no!" and wrapped

NOTES

herself in her own arms and shivered again.

"Kay asked me with alarm, 'If the storm has done that to the Galvez, what is it going to do to us?' But," Ray continued their story, "when we got back to the portable TV they were correcting the mistaken report someone had turned in. The truth was that windows of the top two stories had been blown out and they were moving all the people down to the basement. Nevertheless, the story caused us further anxiety.

"Then the Weather Station announced that the Eye of Elisha was over the San Luis Pass Bridge that connects Galveston with the mainland, ten miles away from us!"

Kay put her hands to her head and described the circumstances, "We didn't think the wind and rain could get any worse, but we were mistaken. It did get worse. There was an eerie feeling in the house, a sort of explosive tension."

Ray said, seriously reflecting, "I reached up and touched the wall and it quivered like jello, very

NOTES

vigorously, under my hand. It scared me. We prayed a lot!"

Ray's word picture was very sobering. "I had not reckoned my walls would explode until now, but rather that they would implode, because the pressure outside was greater than inside the house. But I had been worried that the roof might blow off and leave us to the buffeting of the wind and water. Every few minutes I took the flashlight and went around checking the windows. They were holding."

Continuing, Ray said, "At 3:00 a.m. the winds were at 115 mph, and all of a sudden the loud noises stopped! For about a full minute it was silent. The edge of the Eye was over us! Then the radio said the storm was going up the ship channel toward Houston. We are about fifty miles south of Houston."

"TV coverage was beautiful," exclaimed Kay. "Clear, pretty pictures of Houston showed us the millions of diamonds in the air from pieces of glass and exploding windows in the sky scrapers."

But Raymond was amazed, "Debris was flying

NOTES

everywhere. It looked like a war zone!"

Karen said, "Shortly afterward, the mayor of Houston declared downtown Houston closed for the first time in history!"

"Elisha was on her way and the wind was terrible." Karen added further, "People had taken their shrimp boats up the channel earlier to get them away from the open sea, but a lot of them were destroyed anyway."

Ray described the difference in the sound of the wind as the storm passed away from their home.

"Strangely enough, we could tell the difference in the sound of the wind as it decreased just ten miles per hour. Hurricanes dissipate over the land and by 5:00 a.m. the winds were down to 105 mph again, and something like 200,000 homes were without power in Houston! However their power was restored more quickly than ours here in the rural areas."

Kay explained, "We were without power for ten days, and lost about $1,000 worth of food in our

NOTES

freezers. We lost about half of the barn, but not a single shingle from our house roof, and there was no other damage."

The family was asked, "How did you manage to cook, with the utilities all out?"

Ray said, "We cooked on camping equipment for a few days--and were very thankful to be alive. When Elisha left us behind her we threw our arms around each other and cried and the children said we prayed for about six hours with thanksgiving!

"We know the power of prayer. We did not defy the hurricane, we just were not careful enough in making a wiser decision, but we were protected through it. We kept a prayer in our hearts all the time."

Aunt Jane asked them, "Why do you continue to live in this area? Aren't you afraid of these terrible hurricanes? The season lasts so long. Didn't you tell me the hurricane season is between June and November? That is six months of every year!"

Karen answered by inquiring, "Why do people

NOTES

live in high risk earthquake areas, or in the arctic where it gets so cold? We like where we live. We just work with things."

The Webb family all agreed, "Storm insurance is high along the coast, but family, friends, our work, our land, and the sea breezes every day make living on the Gulf worthwhile. However, the next time there is a hurricane alert, we won't wait! Never again will we try to ride out a hurricane! We'll take off, come back and collect the insurance and start all over again if we have to."

Aunt Jane declared, "My goodness, I believed the old adage that when everything is said and done, few people would trade their own calamities for those of someone else! And I add my thanksgivings to yours.

NOTES

****

Suggested Exercise

1. Have family members tell what the family in this story did to prepare for emergencies accompanying natural disasters.
2 What is the difference between a hurricane WATCH and a hurricane WARNING?
3. What types of disasters were most prevalent in their general location? (Tropical storms, flooding, hurricanes, and possible tornados.)
4. What lessons did you learn from the experiences in this story?
5. Name the emergencies to which your area is most vulnerable.
6. Tell what precautions your family has undertaken to prepare for natural disasters. If you have made no definite plans or preparations, make assignments to discover what preparations are in order. Next, set a date or time to work on and have them completed. This may take months or a perpetual program. See your Welfare and food storage materials.

Draw a picture about this story here, or to build comprehension, write your version of the story on this page.

Where several children are using one book, have them draw a picture or write their story and put their best work in their journals.

NOTES

MIKE FOX AND PATTY

It was like leaving his mother behind, even though she was no longer in the house. Tears welled up and Jonathan looked desperately to his Dad for help to bear this burden. Mother was being left behind, there was no getting around it. Her funeral had been three weeks ago, and it still hurt to be without the heart of their family. No matter where they went to live, it would be without his mother, Pauline.

Jonathan's dad, Matt, had turned to the familiar to find strength to go on without Pauline. With a son to raise alone--but he mustn't think of himself as being alone. There was Jonathan. They would go back to the ranch where he and his wife started their

NOTES

lives together. A summer would give them time to work through some hurts and be together.

A five hour drive found them winding down a dusty, one lane, country road. They had been on ranch property for the last hour's drive, and now they approached an unpainted, two story ranch house.

They parked the truck on the north side of the house in the shade.

Off to the side, slightly down the hill were a corral, a long bunkhouse, some holding pens, a barn, and a shed or two.

The corral was unusually large and had chutes in one direction then another connecting the holding pens for cattle. They would divide selected cattle, drive them through chutes into holding pens until they were ready to drive the herd to the railroad yards. The rest of the cattle was turned loose and they wandered off back to the range.

At the railyards chute ramps ran up to the boxcars and the cattle was loaded.

A large cattle ranch was indeed an institution, a

NOTES

business, an industry almost as big as the state of which it was a part.

"Wow, this is the biggest place I ever saw. Just look! You can see forever." Jonathan, now past his tenth birthday, removed his hand-me-down Stetson, the cowboy hat for all Texans, mopped his forehead on his sleeve and sat up tall in the saddle. He gazed out over the plains. Matt and Jonathan found, saddled and mounted horses to look around a bit before supper.

Matt and Jonathan were excited about working on one of the largest ranches in Texas. This would give them time, and make the missing of Mother easier someday maybe.

"Jonathan," said his father, Matt, "This is just one of the Worsham Ranches. It has sixty thousand acres on it. Can you imagine how large a piece of real estate that is? Think we can handle it?"

Jonathan was impressed and smiled. "No, Sir, I can't guess how big that is. Sounds like a lot."

When Jonathan's mother and Dad were first

NOTES

married they had lived out on the ranch for a while. Jonathan was sure he would learn about the largeness of the ranch by working it with his dad.

"Mr. Worsham says his foreman, Mike Fox, is getting too old to handle everything and he needs us to live out here and help Mike. We have to care for the cattle and keep the windmills working good so they will pump water for the cattle. They range out there--" Matt made a wide sweep with his arm to show Jonathan, "all over the place.

"In the winter, if it snows too much we'll have to take feed out to the stock in the wagon." Matt looked at Jonathan, "You wouldn't mind that too much, would you?"

Jonathan grinned at his dad and said, "No, Sir, I'll be a real cowboy. If you think we can do it, Dad, I guess we can."

"It is important to learn the work well, Jonathan. I've lived on ranches most of my life, but Mike Fox will tell us what he wants us to do for him."

Jonathan and Matt rode out to the barn to

NOTES

stable their horses and to find Mike, who was supposed to be around somewhere.

"Dad, I thought you said they shipped most of the cattle off last week. How many are left for us to tend?" Jonathan was ready to get down to business.

"Son, they shipped forty-four boxcars full of steers on the train to the market. That was the second shipment this year. It leaves sixteen hundred stock cattle for us. That shouldn't be much trouble."

Jonathan was anxious to see this elderly gentleman, Mike Fox, about whom he had heard so much. He hoped he wasn't too old, and that he wouldn't mind if he played with his dog, Patty.

They looked the corral over, found the pig pen and a few chickens but no Mike Fox anywhere.

Matt suggested, "Jonathan, let's go on up to the house and fix some supper for ourselves and for Mike. That's in the bargain too, you know."

"Yes, Sir." Jonathan had been taught that all children replied, when spoken to, with "Yes Sir, or no Sir," or with "Yes Mam, or no Mam". His mother

NOTES

wanted to be sure Jonathan was as polite as any other young Texan, so this response was second nature to Jonathan.

They were twenty miles from the nearest town, but Mr. Worsham had said, "Go to the store for anything you need in the way of supplies, and sign for them. I will pay for them."

Jonathan and Matt were to cook, do the washing and keep the house, besides helping Mike in every way, because of his age. Mike was nearing seventy-five. It had been a hard life, often exposed to the elements, riding horses, branding cattle, shipping them to market, keeping an eye on their safety, their water supply and so on.

They went into the old four room ranch house, called out Mike's name, but there was no answer. Matt showed Jonathan the staircase, and said Jonathan could go up and see their bedroom, while he started a fire in the huge kitchen wood stove.

Mike's bed room and the long kitchen with table and chairs, and a rocker or two, a fire place

NOTES

and empty coal bucket, a desk and kerosene lamp on it about made up the downstairs. A number-two galvanized wash tub was used on Saturday nights for baths, and "the path" behind the house led to the outhouse toilet.

There was also a gun rack holding several rifles on the wall in the kitchen. Above the cook stove there was a food warmer that ran the length of the range. A rounded cover rolled down and hid the food placed on the shelf where it kept warm for a while.

Jonathan came into the kitchen and asked, "Dad, why are all of these plates turned upside down on the table? Look, the knives and forks are in place and there are tin cups turned upside down." Jonathan walked around the table and counted twenty-two places set.

Matt said, "Son, I asked Mike the same question. He said to me, 'Well, that is as good a place as any for them.' Those are for the cowhands Mike hires to round up the cattle every year. He just

NOTES

leaves them there."

"Dad, you just said that Mike doesn't say much. Is he sour on the world?

"Except for when the round ups are taking place," answered his dad, "Mike lives alone and no, he is not angry or sour, just a man of few words, Jonathan."

Jonathan was full of questions. "You said Mike hardly says anything. Why does he do that?"

Matt answered, "Jonathan, we must not make a fuss. He is a good man, and has been the foreman here long before Mr. Carl Worsham was born. Mr. Carl is our boss. He owns the ranches. Mike used to work for Mr. Carl's father, Mr. Dick. Mr. Dick Worsham and Colonel Charles Goodnight came to this county and filed claim on this land years ago." Then Matt added, "You'll like Mike's little dog, Patty."

Jonathan and Matt fixed fried potatoes with onions and cornbread and molasses for their supper, and left plenty in the warmer for Mike. It was getting toward sunset and the barnyard animals needed

NOTES

feed and water, so the pair walked down to the barn, and there was Mike already doing the chores.

"Mike, this is my son, Jonathan. Jonathan, Mr. Fox will find just the right jobs for you. Be sure to take care of them right away."

"Yes, Sir." Jonathan smiled.

Mike glanced at Jonathan for a fleeting moment, nodded, picked up his little tin bucket, filled it with corn and limped slowly out to the pig pen. Jonathan hurried up to Mike Fox and said, "Here, let me get that for you, Sir."

Mike looked at Jonathan momentarily, let him take the bucket of feed, and said, "Two more."

Jonathan watered the pigs and locked the pens while Mike headed for the house to eat his supper. Patty followed him right into the house.

Mike was a short man, bent and wrinkled and nearly bald underneath his weather worn, broad brimmed, ten gallon hat. He didn't growl or frown. He didn't do much of anything but sort of grunt when he bent over.

NOTES

While Mike slowly ate his supper he slipped a crumb or two to Patty who lay on the floor under one end of the table right beside Mike's feet. Jonathan looked Patty over from across the room since she stayed by Mike's side and only lifted her nose and smelled. She didn't come close to Jonathan to check him out. She just stayed by Mike.

Patty weighed about seven or eight pounds, was fourteen years old and could hardly see. Mike just about worshiped Patty. She was his best friend and had been his only companion for years.

Matt told his son when they went up the stairs to bed, "Mike gives Patty a stick of candy every night."

Jonathan liked hearing all about Patty. "Patty has a good nose. When Mike is a mile away, coming in from making the rounds on the ranch, Patty will get up, hold her nose high and sniff. She can smell Mike Fox. She knows when he is coming," said his father, who had long observed this friendship between the man and his dog.

NOTES

Mike Fox was a bachelor and all he knew was ranching. He was a good man, just awfully quiet. Matt explained, "He seldom had anyone to make conversation with over the years. I guess you could say he has had no practice, Jonathan."

The next morning Mike said to Jonathan and Matt, "We'll... take a look." That is all he said.

Jonathan and Matt assumed Mike meant for them to look at the ranch, so they walked with him out to the windmill back of the house.

Mike Fox pointed up to the windmill and made a circle with his arm in different directions and said, "More'n thirty-five miles square."

Jonathan climbed the windmill and looked, but all he could see in the predawn light was grazing land, flat grazing land. Miles and miles away a few low hills were seen in the distance.

When he got down, Matt leaned over and told Jonathan, "Mr. Worsham told me we live and work on the "C" place, where there are only sixty thousand acres. There are a hundred and sixty thousand more

NOTES

acres on the big headquarters ranch." Jonathan's lips puckered and a low whistle came out. He wasn't sure, but that sounded like an awful lot of Texas.

Mike's instructions were just as brief. He said, "Oil 'em, 'n salt the cattle." He patted his little black dog, then added. "Thirty of 'em."

Mike meant there were thirty windmills out there on the range to take care of.

"All right, sir, we'll take some grub and take a look," said Matt. "Can you hold the fort down?" Mike walked back to the house without answering, but with Patty following him.

"Turning to Jonathan, Matt said, "Guess that was a foolish question, Son, after all that is what he has been doing for years--holding the fort down! Might as well saddle the horses. C'mon, Son."

Matt filled Jonathan in on more particulars as they rode along. There were baking powder biscuits and bacon, jerky, some jelly sandwiches, and a dozen boiled eggs wrapped in the saddle bags.

"I know you are used to riding some, but Son,

NOTES

this is going to take us all day. We will have to ride about ten miles today in this direction just to get to the first windmill, so it will be nearly dark before we get back. Can you do that?"

"Yes, Sir. Can we spend the night if we get too tired, Dad?" asked Jonathan.

"Sure, we have blankets, and the horses can eat grass one day." Matt decided spending two days was a good idea. He could show Jonathan the work and do a little sight seeing. Jonathan wished his mother could be along with them.

It was a long hot ride to the first windmill. Just before reaching there, Matt showed Jonathan some of the magnificence of this country, and let him see nature at her best. Living in the city had not acquainted Jonathan with many animals or the way they survive in the open, only the way they lived in a zoo. Ranch life was a wonderful place to find out about the important things in life his dad had said.

Suddenly Matt said, "Dismount, Jonathan! I want you to hand me that dead mesquite branch

NOTES

over there. Watch out for the stickers."

Jonathan did as he was told. Matt tied a white rag to the end and stuck the stick into a prairie dog hole. It stood about eight feet in the air.

"What is this for, Dad?" A gentle breeze waved the white flag in the air.

"You'll see. Give me your hand, Son, I'll give you a hand mounting up, we have some way to go yet."

The two rode along singing cowboy songs and speculating about whether they would find the windmill working and pumping water.

"I am thirsty for fresh water, too, Dad. Look at those steers over there. Are they ours?"

There were about fifteen steers slowly trudging in the same direction they rode, toward the windmill ahead.

Matt nodded yes. "You know, Son, cattle can smell water when it is quite far away. They know where they are going. Just watch them. We will follow and they will lead us right to the windmill.

NOTES

See? There it is around the hill," said Matt.

When they arrived they found half a dozen cows drinking from the tank. They stood in mud at the lower end because the water slowly overflowed. Weeds grew close to the tank in the mud.

"The windmill pumps the water when the wind blows, and as long as it blows. No one is here to turn the water off, but at least the tank is full most of the time. "There is plenty of water in the tank now," said Jonathan. A round corrugated tin held about two feet of water. It seemed clean enough, but there was sand at the bottom and green moss was growing to the sides of the tin. The massive tub was about fifteen feet across and water from the windmill slowly ran through a pipe that jutted out over the tank. It was from this pipe that Jonathan and Matt washed their hands, and drank from them.

"Splash some on your face, Son, it'll cool you off." Matt demonstrated, "and fill your canteen."

Matt took out his tool sack from the saddle bag and started climbing the windmill. "Oops! Better

NOTES

bring me those nails, Jonathan. There is a step loose here. I'll have to fix it before you can climb up."

Matt had an oil can and a grease can looped through his belt so he could oil or grease the workings up high on the windmill.

When he finished, Matt called to Jonathan to climb up to the platform below the fan with him. The platform was about twenty feet above the ground and had a hand rail around it for safety.

"Now, from here you can see the stick with the white flag that we stuck in the ground. Do you see anything? Look good everywhere."

"Oh yes, Sir! Dad, what are they doing?" Jonathan was very excited.

"Shhh, Jonathan. Sound carries on the wind easily. You will scare them away. Now, tell me, what do you see?" asked Matt.

"Looks like deer, Dad. Oh, there come some more way over there. Are they deer, Dad?"

"Jonathan, those are antelope. You have never seen antelope have you?" asked Matt.

NOTES

"Nope, never did, Sir. Where are they all coming from? Where are they going?" whispered Jonathan.

"They are curious, Jonathan. They want to know what that thing is. All they see out here are other animals and some birds and snakes. If you will be quiet and keep your arms still, you will see dozens of them in a few minutes. See, over there! There come some more. They can see that white flag for miles."

"I wish Mama could see the antelope, Dad. Do you think she can?"

"Let me tell you something about your Mom, Jonathan. She loved animals. That is a good thing to remember about her. She never harmed animals, was never mean to them." Matt could see a little of Pauline's way with animals in Jonathan.

"Dad, wasn't she afraid of them at all?"

"No, Son. She treated them like people. She talked to them and made friends with them easily. Why, the shyest dog around would soon be eating

NOTES

out of her hand. They could tell she wouldn't hurt them."

Then Matt added, "I've got something to show you later that made your Mama shiver with fright though."

"What's that, Dad?" asked Jonathan.

"I'll show you tomorrow. It is just this side of the creek." Matt motioned to descend the ladder.

"Son, let's get a good drink and eat a couple of boiled eggs. There is a trail leading off in this direction." Matt pointed the way. "It goes to the next windmill. We'll get started." Jonathan loved being with his Dad.

"Dad, you said to watch out for the salt licks. Is that one of them over there?" Jonathan pointed to a block of something on the ground. It looked as if it were salt and red pepper mixed together in a solid mass.

Matt assured Jonathan that he had found one. "It has been licked down to half its size, and there is only one more block around. You know what this

NOTES

means don't you, Jonathan?"

Jonathan shook his head, "No, Sir."

"That means we need to bring the wagon next week, with a load of salt. The cattle have to have salt licks around."

"Why, Dad?" asked Jonathan.

"All wild animals need salt in their diets, and if there are not enough natural licks around--ones they usually find in some rock formations, then we have to provide salt for them," explained Matt.

Still not satisfied, Jonathan asked again, "Why do they like red pepper in their salt, Dad?"

"Jonathan, that's not pepper. It is a mineral, just like salt is. Sure looks like pepper, doesn't it?"

Matt and Jonathan ate and mounted their horses and started down the trail that led toward a few low hills on the horizon.

"This part of Texas is wide and sometimes ribbed with gullies made by floods the thunderstorms bring. Rain drenches the thirsty red sand and grasses, and if it rains too fast and too hard, it

NOTES

causes flooding."

Matt pointed to the gully ahead of them. Their horses went down into the big dry ditch, then climbed up out of the gully on the other side.

"Rain leaves gullies where the sand is washed away," explained Matt. "If you ever get caught out on the range during a thunderstorm, stay out of the gullies. You'd get swept away in a hurry, Son. No good cowboy tempts nature to do him harm."

Mesquite trees, picturesque but squatty and thorny, dotted the countryside. Big formations of rocks grew out of the ground near the cedars and Jonathan found smaller rocks made pretty good tables on which to eat their supper.

When they stopped to camp late in the day, Jonathan stood on a large rock and untied the blanket behind his saddle. The blanket slid off and Jonathan turned to spread it on the ground where he was going to sleep.

"Freeze, Jonathan!" His dad shouted curtly.

Immediately, Jonathan heard a blast of noise

NOTES

and a bullet sped past him, and hit the big rock. Jonathan looked and there was a huge rattlesnake slithering off into the mesquites. His Dad had missed the snake, but if Matt had not warned Jonathan, he might have put the blanket down right beside the snake, and rattlers strike like lightning!

Both were silent for a moment, then Matt said, "It's all right, Son. He's gone. I doubt he'll be back. But when you are out here, you have to always be on the watch for snakes. This is where they live, especially in the rocks where it is cool.

Jonathan thought there sure was a lot to learn about ranching, but he was seeing a side of his father he had never noticed before. Dad had just always gone to work in the morning, in a shirt and tie, and Jonathan had gone to school. About the only things they had ever talked about was how to fix flat tires on his bike, swimming safety, ball games and mowing the lawn. Boy, his dad was sure smart. He knew so much about things and animals--and he hadn't forgotten about Jonathan's mother, which was

NOTES

important to Jonathan.

Matt and Jonathan chewed on some beef jerky and ate sandwiches while they lay on the blanketed ground by their fire. Each propped a foot on the knee of his other leg and felt the warmth of the fire on their seats while they talked about Texas skies, where God had hung the biggest stars in the world and an oversize moon just for Texans. They talked about the howl of coyotes in the distance. Camping out had to be just about the greatest thing in the world when you were with your dad.

The next morning they checked another windmill and continued their journey toward home and Mike and Patty. After a few miles on the way, mid afternoon found them again ready for a rest.

Matt said, "Before we head back too far in this direction, I want to show you something really interesting, Jonathan. See over there by those trees and rocks in front of the small hill?" Matt pointed in the right direction.

"Yes, Sir. Looks like there is a hole in the side

NOTES

of the hill. Is there one?" asked Jonathan.

"You have good eyes, Jonathan. That is nearly a mile away. That's where we are headed. Come on, I'll beat you."

Matt let Jonathan set the pace for the race, and when they pulled up below the hill where the hole was, Jonathan, out of breath said, "Dad,...it is a... bigger hole...than I thought. What is it...a mine?"

"Just a shaft into the mine, Jonathan," explained his dad. "Let's get down and rest for a while. I feel like finishing off the grub we brought along, and have a drink."

Matt handed Jonathan a couple of the eggs and a little salt and pepper rolled up in a piece of brown paper.

"See these eggs, Son? The first time your mother and I visited out here we came in the wagon on a picnic with a couple of people who were visiting from town. We brought lots of boiled eggs and some sandwiches. Boiled eggs remind me of those times."

Jonathan was silent. His dad missed his

NOTES

mother too.

Looking around Matt continued, "This is called Dead Horse Pasture and there are old copper mines around here. Your mother and I would spend the day hiking around and your mother was very curious about that old shaft up there. Its opening is about ten or fifteen feet deep and very dark."

"Did you go in it, Dad?" inquired Jonathan.

"Oh, no, Son, there would be rattle snakes in there. It would be very dangerous, but come, I will show you something very interesting about that shaft."

They climbed the hill to the big hole in the ground and stood outside of it looking closely. It was fun exploring with his son.

"D'you see anything, Jonathan?" asked Matt.

"Just a big dark hole and some rocks and dirt, Sir." Jonathan looked carefully.

"Are you sure that's all you see?"asked Matt.

"Yes, Sir. That's all."

Then Matt stretched out his hand toward

NOTES

Jonathan, "Here, take this pebble and throw it into the hole--right there into the opening."

Jonathan tossed the rock just inside of the cave. Immediately the walls of the cave came alive with millions of grandaddy spiders! There were so many the ground vibrated with motion for several minutes until they quieted down again.

"Wow! What was that? What was that wiggling all over the place?" Jonathan was about ready to take off down the hill.

"That is what your mother said when she saw them. There are millions of Daddy Longlegs in there, on the floor and walls and the ceiling. Sometimes they are called Harvestman, but they are just long legged spiders. They won't hurt you. Throw another rock in there and this time watch them closely."

Jonathan picked up another rock, tossed it in and observed the commotion that took place. "They make the ground shake, Dad. They're everywhere! Wow! Did it scare Mom?"

Matt explained, "Even though she loved

NOTES

animals, she didn't like spiders, or snakes. But it is interesting to see them in their natural habitat, isn't it, Son?"

After another pebble-throw or two, the pair returned to their horses and rode off toward home. It had been a long day, and it was good to see the ranch house beneath the windmill in the distance.

When Matt and Jonathan came from the barn where they had fed, curried, and watered the horses, they saw Mike Fox down on his knees near the windmill doing something. They went over to see what was up.

There was Mike's little dog, Patty, on the ground with her whole side torn open and Mike was trying to sew her up with a needle and thread.

"Mike! What happened, Sir?" asked Matt, who knelt down and held Patty so Mike could work better.

"Fed the hogs...," Mike sniffed tears back, "She crawled under the fence. Couldn't see too well. Hog made a slash at her--," Mike wiped his nose on the sleeve of his shirt. Big tears ran down his long grey

NOTES

whiskers and dropped on the ground as he worked to save Patty's life.

The two men worked for about an hour and Matt said, "That's about as good as we can do, Sir. Let's bind her up good and we'll just have to wait and see what happens. Poor little faithful dog."

Matt tried to comfort Mike Fox, but that was the last Mike had to say about the accident. He was too upset to talk.

As old as Mike was, he still got up during the night and kept checking on Patty, his wonderful little friend. But the wound was too severe, there had been too much loss of blood, and probably infection had set in overnight. The next morning Patty died.

When Jonathan came down to breakfast the next morning he saw Mike out in the front yard digging a grave for Patty. It was too hard for Jonathan to help with the grave. It was too soon after his mother's funeral. But he walked out to where Mike was digging, put his hand on Mike's arm for a minute when Mike stopped to catch his breath. Mike

NOTES

was crying. Jonathan ran back to the house with his own flood of tears.

Later that night Matt and Jonathan saw Mike Fox pick up the receiver of the their home made telephone, which was connected only to Mr. Worsham's home in Henrietta, Texas. It was seldom ever used. He cranked the handle of the phone several rounds and waited. Mrs. Worsham answered the phone and Mike said only two words, "Patty's dead". Then Mike hung up the receiver.

Jonathan and Matt sat out on the porch steps that night and talked about how it was to lose mothers and friends like Patty.

Jonathan said, "Dad, I'm sure heaven can't be heaven if there aren't mothers and our friends and the animals up there too. But, Dad, it sure is good to have more mothers, and friends like you and Mike, down here. Thanks for taking me with you to see part of the ranch, Dad. I love you."

Matt put his arm around Jonathan's shoulder and held him close.

NOTES

Jonathan said, "We will cheer Mike up and help him all we can. You and I know how Mike needs friends now, don't we, Dad?"

Jonathan was growing up fast. His father commended him, "Son, you have learned a lot this year, what with your mother being so sick and going. Now you have learned that one of the best ways to get to feeling better when you have lost someone you love is to find someone who needs a friend and love them so they will feel better too."

A big Texas moon showered a smile of blessings down upon a father and his small son who were lonesome, but full of love for each other and their friends, Mike Fox and Patty.

NOTES

****

Suggested Exercise

1. A long time ago all youngsters responded to their elders (grown up people) with a very polite "Yes Mam", "No Mam", or "Yes sir", "No sir." If they wanted to ask a question, they would say, "Mam...?"

It was the mark of a well-mannered lady or gentleman, young or old. It also automatically showed honor and respect. It said in essence, "I have respect for what I expect you to be, even if I do not know you."

If you really want to get attention or a polite reply from someone, establish this habit for all your communications. Military leaders learned long ago that respect shown through communication made a lot of difference in attitude and behavior.

Do you think it would be fun to start a new positive, polite trend that might lead people to having and showing more respect for each other again?

After all, you were important and unique enough to be different in many ways from the world already! Some of you go to private schools, are a Mormon, dare to be drug free, do not swear, wear modest clothing, are gang free, keep the Sabbath, and are honestly trying to improve yourself daily.

2. Even grown ups speak with these greetings when talking with older friends, neighbors, or strangers. What are some good ideas for starting a great new being-polite campaign?

Draw a picture about this story here, or to build comprehension, write your version of the story on this page.

Where several children are using one book, have them draw a picture or write their story and put their best work in their journals.

PART TWO

To Children

My older son, without having read the manuscript, said to me, "Remember, Mother, that young children were born with tenderness and love and trust. Don't let them think you believe they have abandoned those feelings."

How grateful I am for that reminder. In case one word in these stories should leave you with that impression, I do remember that you came here with those wonderful virtues. Will you remember that sometimes the stresses and responsibilities of parenthood cause a display of impatience and anger and sometimes a demonstration of unjust ways of correcting and caring for you?

I rejoice that you still have big corners of your hearts that are gentle, loving and trusting. My prayer is that adults will look at you and be able to see just another person, but a younger, tender person who is trying to learn, to grow and continue to be good. I pray that parents will prayerfully remember that their demonstrations of love and their efforts to guide must forever be tempered with justice and fairness and a strong testimony of the gospel of Christ.

Will you, our children, respect our better natures, and forgive us when we make mistakes? Will you help us in our responsibility to pass on the wisdom that experience and knowledge has given us?

The Lord loves parents too. He is forgiving and knows it is difficult to be perfect parents. Because He loves us He gives us help and understanding when we search for it in the scriptures and in prayer.

We welcomed you and thanked you for coming to live with us. We do love you. You are precious gifts. You bring us much happy ness.

Will you take our hands and retreat with us from all forms of worldly impatience, intolerance, hate and violence, and together we will carry on--with gentleness?

NOTES

A CHRISTMAS GREETING: THE GEESE

Back in Massachusetts a mother stood by her large dining room window enjoying the first display of winter. It was a lovely sight. She lived near a shallow, inland body of water, and snow with bitter winds had rushed in over night leaving a magical scene. Ice cycles dropped from the limbs of bushes and trees and soft snow had left pillows covering the marsh grass. A cold but light wind continued to make its presence known.

As the mother stood watching she noticed white ice had formed along the banks and reached toward the middle of the stream. Something dark on

NOTES

the river prompted her to pick up her binoculars and look more closely.

There, very still, sat a large goose with its wings close to its sides. It did not bob up and down as was usual when birds sat on moving water. Upon further study the young woman could see that the bird was sitting still because its feet were frozen under the ice which had so quickly formed over night.

Perplexed about what to do for the poor bird, she almost immediately heard the honking sound of a flight of geese, in formation headed south.

They were free and about their own journey, but suddenly when they flew over the ice bound bird below, the leader banked to the left and with his school of birds in pursuit, circled around the bird frozen in place. Another circle brought the flock down onto the ice around the ill fated goose and they all began to pick at the ice with their beaks. Long necks lifted, curved, and drummed at the ice again and again breaking it up gradually until the cold dark

NOTES

bird was free.

The large flock lifted their wings and took flight again. They circled once as if inviting, encouraging the bird below to join them. The freed bird, a little stiff and awkward at first, soon took to the air flapping its wings double time until it caught up with the v-shaped flock on its way.

Spiritually touched, the woman watched the flock till it disappeared, lowered her binoculars and said to herself, " What a lesson to start the day! If birds can do it so can people."

The young woman was buoyed by the compassion and the collective efforts of the flock to assist one in need. That day she was going to find someone who needed a lift, a helping hand. She was reminded in her heart of the admonition of the Savior to serve Him by serving each other. Besides she wanted to experience the wonderful feeling, the joy that seemed manifest in the geese when they took flight. They could not leave one of their own behind in pain or facing a cruel end. Today she would lift the

NOTES

pain or touch the heart of another.

May our Christmas be extra special when we find a way to be a better goose!

(Based on a story told in a Sacrament Meeting)

****

Suggested Exercise

Q. Did you learn that circumstances can change quickly and over night in this story?

Q. Have you ever helped an animal or bird in distress? Tell about it.

Q. What acts of kindness have you learned from animals?

Q. What is this story's main message?

Q. Who do you know whose "feet may be frozen in the ice" this Christmas? What can you do about it?

Draw a picture about this story here, or to build comprehension, write your version of the story on this page.

Where several children are using one book, have them draw a picture or write their story and put their best work in their journals.

NOTES

LISTENING TO THE CORN GROW

Hunger pangs gnawed at Lonnie's stomach. "I wonder if ants and bugs will be in my lunch again today?" He asked aloud.

It was Lonnie's twelfth summer. It seemed that weeds had multiplied over night. Lonnie had been pulling weeds on the family farm since before the sun had touched the mountain top. He had been hungry for an hour and thought the crew would never stop to eat, but Lonnie found his Mom had solved the ants and bugs problem by packing his lunch in an empty syrup bucket with a tight lid on it, and Lonnie had no trouble devouring the food. He did save a jelly sandwich for later in the afternoon, but by day's end, Lonnie was too tired to be hungry.

When his dad and the others went back

NOTES

through the fields on the flatbed wagon drawn by the tractor, Lonnie decided to jump off the wagon by the creek and get a nice cool drink and rest for a while. Evening chores wouldn't seem so hard after a little break in the shade, besides, something was on Lonnie's mind.

All week Lonnie had wondered what his Sunday School teacher, Mrs. Miller, meant when she said a "still, small, voice" would whisper things to them? The subject of the Holy Ghost, and His teaching you right from wrong was not exactly unfamiliar to Lonnie, but he was not sure how all this worked.

Lonnie was not sure he had ever experienced an encounter with the Holy Ghost or if he would have recognized it, if he really had. The last time he had asked a question in Sunday School the boys snickered. Lonnie hadn't minded that too much, still, he seemed to be the only one in class to ask questions, and he hated to be the dumb one all the time! Questions about this voice, this Holy Spirit,

NOTES

now arose in his mind more frequently.

After wetting his face in the cold stream and drinking his fill, Lonnie sat on a rock near the bank of the creek. Suddenly he remembered that in the evenings critters from the woods came there to drink also. Lonnie decided to walk over into the edge of the corn field. The animals might not see him there, or smell his scent if the wind were in the right direction. If he sat very still he would be able to watch them drink in the creek.

The air was heavy, but Lonnie settled down between two rows of corn and just lay on the soft plowed earth and looked into the blue sky. The coolness of early dusk became very pleasant. In all the stillness a slight breeze stirred the air. Rest was so welcome.

Mrs. Miller had often mentioned the still, small voice. "She must want us to hear it awful bad, or she wouldn't keep bringing it up", thought Lonnie.

"There must be a catch to it all. Why don't teachers tell you how to find out about these things?

NOTES

All she said was that if you were about to engage in bad activities the voice might warn you once or twice, and if you didn't pay attention, it might not come to you again." That made sense.

A still voice? A small voice? How can a voice be still? Lonnie wondered what a small voice was like.

Mom had said, "When it speaks to you, you will know. You have to learn to listen for the voice. Sometimes it seems a long time before answers come, or for you to hear the voice."

And when Lonnie asked his Dad, who had to think about it for a few minutes, he finally replied, "Well, Son, it's hard to explain. When you really need to have help, the voice just comes. It comes one way to one person and sometimes another way to someone else. It is true that it can be heard very clearly, yet, sometimes it..., well it is...kind of like... listening to the corn grow!"

Lonnie thought he had nearly SEEN the corn grow. It grows so fast. When he planted his own

NOTES

patch last year, he measured the same stalks in the middle of the row and found that each day they had grown several inches. That is fast! Boys don't grow that fast! But Lonnie had to admit he had never HEARD the corn grow.

As Lonnie lay quietly in the tall corn, he closed his eyes and really gave listening a try. He certainly was too tired to be getting into mischief, so maybe he was eligible for some help.

In the peaceful, cool of the evening he actually heard small crackles and squeaks. As the long, trailing leaves of the corn emerged from around the stalks, and the stalks SLOWLY reached higher and higher into the sky, there would have to be growing sounds. He could see with his mind's eye that the ears of corn needed more room to expand, and so the ears scrunched against the leaves and stems to emerge a little bit more, and a little bit more. Then, as if a light had turned on in a dark room, Lonnie exclaimed aloud, "You CAN HEAR THE CORN GROW! I hear it! I hear it!"

NOTES

Lonnie listened minutes more to be sure he wasn't just dreaming or imagining all this. He fought to keep the excitement from spoiling this wonderful moment of discovery.

Immediately words began forming in Lonnie's mind. The general message, or idea, began to unfold. Lonnie slowly began to understand what was actually happening. With a gentle grin, his heart leaped within him! His eyes widened and he looked up and exclaimed aloud again, "So that is how it is!"

Lonnie repeated aloud the words that had come to his mind: "YOU HAVE A NEED, AND YOU ASK TO KNOW. THEN YOU REALLY LISTEN." He mustn't forget them. The Holy Ghost himself had shown Lonnie how "it works"!

Lonnie leaped into the air with excitement he could no longer hold! The still, small voice had come. It had come to *him*! "It is still and small...so quiet. I did hear...or I felt...and I saw the words in my thoughts for real!" confessed Lonnie. "You DO KNOW when it happens, just as Mom said."

NOTES

Then to memorize the message, he kept turning it over and over in his head: "You will hear the voice when you have a need, when you ask to know about something, then you listen to recognize the answer when it comes. Hummmm," he repeated, "You have a need, and you ask to know, then you really listen, or as Dad would say, you `pay attention!'"

Lonnie thought he would never forget that day or his wonderful, new understanding from the Holy Ghost. He reasoned that the Holy Ghost could even help you when you hadn't out-right asked about something--if you really wanted to be good, to do right. Maybe the Holy Ghost knew you needed help before you knew you did! Wow!

An unmistaken, indescribably warm feeling accompanied the wonderful discovery. A feeling said to him, "It's true. It's true!"

Lonnie asked aloud, "I wonder--could this great feeling be `the burning in the bosom' the scriptures talk about? Sure feels like it. I'll have to ask Mom,"

NOTES

Lonnie decided.

Continuing to ponder the meaning of the words that had come to him, Lonnie figured that a fellow just about always has needs, and he guessed that praying regularly was the asking part, and that when you had to make a decision or something, you had better really listen for that still, small voice inside to help you out. You gotta recognize it when it comes.

Lonnie's heart was so full of gratitude, he lifted his eyes once again toward heaven and said simply, "Thanks."

No longer tired from the day's hard work, Lonnie stepped lively through the fields, along the ditch banks, toward home.

"Moms sure are smart," Lonnie thought. "And so are Dads who know a boy needs to be still and think about things a little--while he listens to the corn grow."

NOTES

****

Suggested Exercise

Q. Do you recognize the still small voice every time it speaks to you? (Usually not every time. We should practice listening for its help after we have prayed, and keep our prayer in mind the next few days while we are waiting for answers. He can direct us all along our way.)
Q. Is it dumb to ask questions?
Q. Have you ever had a strong feeling not to do a particular something?
Q. Did you not do the thing you were thinking of, or did you go ahead and do it? What happened?
Q. Were you aware that the strong feeling not to do what you had in mind was from the Holy Ghost?
Q. Did you ever get an idea to do something good for someone and followed through and did it?
Q. Describe the feeling you had afterward. Do you know what that good feeling is called? (The "Fruits", or the results, "of obedience." When you obey the still small voice, the rewards, results, or fruits are those wonderful feelings afterward.)
Q. Why doesn't the Holy Ghost tell us every single thing to do? (Maybe he does, in that he reveals all truth to us so we can make choices, but he also respects our free agency, our own intelligence and creativity. It is the Devil or Satan who would want to make us do everything.)

Draw a picture about this story here, or to build comprehension, write your version of the story on this page.

Where several children are using one book, have them draw a picture or write their story and put their best work in their journals.

NOTES

THE HOLY GHOST AND RED FLAGS

Jimmy chewed on his tongue as he tried to fit a headband on his six year old sister's head. "Be still, Susie. Now, don't take it off, O.K.? Here, Aaron, hold this box of stuff."

It was Family Home Evening night and Jimmy's turn to give the lesson. At twelve, you just naturally have all these ideas down pat. It just takes some doing to get cooperation from everyone.

Dad sat up in his easy chair and announced, "I guess you can see that it's Jimmy's turn to conduct the activity, and boy, he doesn't mess around! Jimmy is ready to go. I just want to say I love you all. Thank you for coming down on time tonight. O.K. Jimmy, it is all yours. Who is giving the prayer?"

"Mother's turn, Dad, if that's O.K...?"

NOTES

"Let us have prayer before you finish handing out your things, Jimmy." Each turned and knelt at his chair and became quiet. Mother always said such beautiful prayers. No one was sure the Lord wasn't standing at the doorway and would answer mother at any moment. Prayer felt good when Mother said it.

Jimmy thanked his Mother and immediately set out to put his business in order. "Aaron, let me have the box, please."

"Now, Dad, you take this set of stories and when I tell you, read one of them. Here, this is yours, Mother." Mother took her zig-zagged piece of paper lightning. It was usually easier to get the grownups to go along with things.

"They sure are short stories, Jimmy. I think I can handle that!" Dad looked at the three-by-eight inch pieces of paper with scrawled longhand on them.

"I know, Dad, they are just little skits--but don't read them till I give you the rules." Jimmy turned to Lyle, his fourteen year old brother, and gave him six

NOTES

short sticks with pieces of red paper triangles glued to them. "These are red flags, Lyle. Now be careful and don't mess 'em up....please."

Bridget asked, "Don't I get something, Jimmy?"

"Sure, you hold this, Bridget."

"What's this?" Bridget wrinkled her nose as she examined a strip of blue paper over which the flat piece of chalk had been drawn a few times. It almost resembled a cloud. Jimmy leaned over and whispered into her ear, but that only brought a question to her eyes!

"Fog? A stupor of thought?" Bridget turned the paper upside down and around trying to make sense of it.

Sarah, an older sister was handed a bright ball of sunshine; it was a round yellow piece of paper, and Aaron was given a fishing pole. "Be careful, Aaron, and hold the pole up so it won't stick someone."

"Now here is the way it goes, everybody. Dad reads one skit, and when you hear any part of the

NOTES

story that applies to your symbol hold it up real high. The light or sunshine represents intelligence or the light of Jesus. The lightning, which is...." Jimmy had to look at his notes to remember what it was called, "a sudden streak of pure knowledge down from heaven. The fog represents a stupor of thought, and a red flag represents the warnings of the Holy Ghost. Hold your symbol up high and tell us why you think it applies. Got it?"

Proudly Jimmy orchestrated this activity. He had worked all week to put it together, with his mother's help here and there.

"O.K. Dad, read the first skit, please. Now, everybody listen so you will know if you..if your symbol is being talked about. I'll help you. O.K. start now, Dad." Jimmy sat in his chair to listen.

Sarah asked, "Aren't we going to have a song, Jimmy?"

"I couldn't think of one, and I am tired of everyone choosing 'Carry On'. We'll sing while we eat the pop corn."

NOTES

Dad grinned at Mother and guessed each person conducting was in charge of their portion of Family Home Evening.

The first story began. Once upon a time Lyle was getting his lessons, but when he....!

Up went the paper Bridget had! She said with a grin, "Stupor of thought!" Everyone giggled. It was fun to tease Lyle.

Jimmy admonished her, "Come on, Bridget. This is serious."

Bridget said she would watch it.

On with the story: Lyle was getting his lessons when all of a sudden he remembered that he had gotten pretty low scores on his last two papers and he didn't want to be kicked off the tennis team. So he decided to stay up late if he had to and really put forth effort---.

Up went the bright ball of sunshine, or light Sarah was holding.

Jimmy asked, "Why, Sarah?"

"Well, that was a good idea, it was positive

NOTES

and...well, he was walking in the light when he made the decision to do better with his lessons."

"Good, Sarah." Dad encouraged.

"Looks like this is a continuation of the same story only a different turn," said Dad as he looked further at his papers.

However, Lyle wasn't as bright as he used to be so changed his mind about putting extra time on lessons!

"Uh-oh," said Lyle, "There I go again! I knew I shouldn't have given in to temptation. Here is a red flag."

Everyone laughed at Lyle's admission.

"Put your red flag in Susie's head band, Lyle." directed Jimmy.

"Why?" asked Susie.

Because if the Holy Ghost gives you the feeling that you have made the wrong decision, that is a warning and you should be seeing a red flag or warning sign in your mind!" Jimmy explained.

"Ohhhh, I see." Everyone's head nodded.

NOTES

"O.K. Dad, keep going," instructed Jimmy.

"All right. Let's see..., so Lyle asked Aaron if he wanted to go down to the creek by the pasture and catch some fish before supper."

Aaron, an older brother who was partially blind, spoke up immediately and warned as if the story were taking place that very day. "Oh, no, Lyle, the water has been flooding. There is a big mud slide down there!" He reached toward Lyle and asked, "May I borrow one of your red flags--going fishing now would be disastrous!" Aaron put a red flag in Susie's headband and sat down.

Lyle took up the role playing as if the story really were happening now and said, "Oh, Aaron, we'll be careful. Come on. If it is too muddy to fish, we will just come home."

On with the story. So Aaron and Lyle got their fishing poles and though Aaron was reluctant to go, he loved being with his brother--

Aaron picked up on the live story again and said, "Let's pray about it, Lyle, before we go on."

NOTES

Without the notes to rely upon, Dad picked up on the "live" story too and described what might have happened next...The humid chill of the misty day caused Lyle to lean up against a tree while he said a short prayer, asking if it would be O.K. to go down to the creek. After his prayer, which was sincere enough--

Bridget jumped up and raised her blue foggy paper representing stupor of thought, "Lyle didn't get any answer at all, just a stupor of thought...and he should have known for sure not to go after that!"

The family had role-played often in their family get-togethers. They referred to themselves as the Anderson Summer Stock Theater because they prized their ability to imagine a role and what would happen next. Each took a turn and developed his own twist to the story line being read by their Dad.

Jimmy was not surprised at this turn of events and though he was tempted to get them back on his slant of the story he had prepared for Dad to read, he did not say anything and let the live role playing

NOTES

ride.

Lyle said, "Well, we won't go fishing. We'll just walk down and see the mud slide, Aaron."

Susie said, "Lyle, you still didn't get the message. You are still going to the creek. How many warnings does the Holy Ghost have to give you before you heed it? Better give me another flag."

Dad soberly added, "I think Susie is especially in tune tonight. She remembered when the boys stood by the tree and prayed and got no particular answer. They should have known not to pursue their plans until or unless they felt a peace about going to the mud slide. That was good thinking, Susie."

"Yeah," said Susie who felt her headband to see if the first red flags were still secure. Lyle put a third red flag in her hair.

Mother raised her hand and added, "Meanwhile, back in the kitchen I was frying chicken and all of a sudden I had such a wonderful feeling come over me. The thought was as clear as a bell--as if someone spoke it to me. It said, 'Today,

NOTES

your sons will learn a lesson they will never forget!'"

And Mother held up her own lightning-flash paper and Jimmy immediately cried out, "It was a sudden streak of pure knowledge from heaven!"

"You are right, Jimmy," Mother smiled. "I believe the warm feeling, instead of a panicked one, was telling me that whatever was going to happen to teach the lesson would not be fatal. We'll see."

Sarah said, "I am upstairs bringing down the laundry and something tells me that after I take the laundry down to the utility room, I should check on the boys who went down to the creek instead of getting their lessons."

Bridget said, "Sarah, you must have had a prompting from the Holy Ghost because you usually are thinking of yourself--no offense--when you get busy..., so I think the bright sunshine, or light of the Holy Ghost and Jesus should be raised."

Mother added, "Sarah might not say much about such things, but she does tuck you kids under her wing like an old mother hen. She does think of

NOTES

you, but I am sure the Holy Ghost did plant the seed to check on the boys, Bridget. You are right. Up goes the Light of the Sun."

Sarah picked up on the story and spoke of herself finding a disaster when she went to check on the boys. "When I got to the bank near the mud slide down by the creek, sure enough, there was Aaron furiously and frantically digging mud away from Lyle with his bare hands. Lyle had ventured onto the unbroken portion of the hill to look down over the mud slide when the bank gave way and before they knew it, Lyle slid down the hill with mud washing down over him and he was half covered with mud when the slide came to a halt!"

Sarah thought she might as well make this good, so added to the drama, "I ran to them and told Aaron to grab Lyle's arm sticking above the mud and I would pull his hand and maybe we could both get him out."

This was such an exciting story everyone was caught up in it and Susie asked with no little anxiety,

NOTES

"Did you get him out?"

Jimmy said, "Sure, Susie. Pretend to us how the story might have ended...go ahead, think of a good ending."

Susie put her finger on her chin and thought for a moment. "Well, they got Lyle out of the mud and brought him home and squirted him with the hose to clean the mud off, then we all said prayer 'cause we were thankful he was all right!"

"Yea!" They all cheered for Susie. She had a good ending to the story. Sarah got up and took the red flags out and placed the bright sunshine light inside the headband!

But Dad found that the moment was a wonderful teaching time.

"Jimmy, you have done yourself proud. That was a great lesson. Let me say a couple of things. First, you all caught the vision of paying attention to the still small voice of warning, didn't you? Jimmy's choice of lessons was great. This was such an important thing for us to learn.

NOTES

I was proud of the way you picked up on the subtle but definite ways we are warned by the Holy Ghost. We do have to be prayerful. We do have to be in tune to catch these helps.

Heavenly Father is so good to us. He sent the Holy Ghost to us to guide us when we get caught up with our own ideas and plans. And as we found out by our pretend skit, if we do not pay attention to the warnings, we will have to suffer the consequences. Lyle and Aaron could have easily lost their lives, couldn't they?

"And all the while, Mother knew, also by the still small voice, that they would be saved by the mercy of the Lord, but that they would learn a valuable lesson. Did they? Did we?"

Dad looked around at his fine family and said to his wife. "We do have mighty fine children. Each one is smart, loving, handsome and beautiful, but most of all they are ours."

To the children he asked, "What was the main thing you learned from Jimmy's lesson tonight?"

NOTES

Sarah raised her hand. "Dad, I think Jimmy showed us that the Holy Ghost has red flags that help us recognize He is trying to tell us something important--"

Aaron spoke thoughtfully, "When we have that little light go on in our minds, so to speak, it is His red flag trying to warn us to stop!

"You are right, Aaron. Good insight, Son. I hope all of us will pay close attention from now on to the Holy Ghost and his red flags.

****

Suggested Exercise

1. Please turn in your scriptures to Ether 2:15 and D&C 1:33 to see what it has to say about the spirit of the Lord as it works through the Holy Ghost.
2. Explain what we mean by red flags in this story.
3. How do we feel inside when the Holy Ghost is trying to warn us not to do something, go somewhere, or say something?
4. Tell a story you have heard about someone having listened to the still small voice. That story could be something like the following: Once a man was driving up Provo Canyon with all his family in the car. All of a sudden something said to him, "STOP!"

Automatically the man pulled to a stop and drove to the side of the road. Everybody in the car wondered what was going on but before they could ask, immediately a big semitrailer truck swung around the next corner out of control and going very fast. His brakes were not working and the man and his family would have no doubt been killed right then if he had not instantly obeyed the "Stop!" he heard from the still, small voice!

Draw a picture about this story here, or to build comprehension, write your version of the story on this page.

Where several children are using one book, have them draw a picture or write their story and put their best work in their journals.

NOTES

THE IMPORTANCE OF OBEDIENCE

Obedience to righteous laws and principles is so important that if *you want to live for eternities in a world where there is happiness and order*, where no one steals or lies or harms you or your possessions, where everyone keeps his word and can be counted on to carry his share of the load, then *you* must learn to live this way also!

You cannot go to that world if you are going to be out of place. You must follow righteous rules, be as righteous as others or you won't be allowed there. You have to prove yourself first. There are no try-outs allowed there, you are trying out now. You have to pass the test here and now.

We must start with little things. Imagine the golden streets of heaven being littered! Can you

NOTES

imagine litter-bugs there? We have to begin now never throwing gum wrappers, pop cans, or school papers anywhere but into waste baskets where they can be disposed of properly.

I promise that if you adopt the habit faithfully of not littering, no matter where in this world you are, when you pick up litter or stop yourself from littering, the thought of no litter in heaven will come to you--and you will feel GOOD, mighty good!.

****

Suggested Exercise

1. List three things you personally need to practice on doing better if you expect to live in your own inherited kingdom where everyone obeys all the rules.
2. Are there any rules you think ought to be added to family rules to help your family prepare to live in heaven?

Draw a picture about this story here, or to build comprehension, write your version of the story on this page.

Where several children are using one book, have them draw a picture or write their story and put their best work in their journals.

NOTES

THE SONG OF REDEEMING LOVE

"Have ye felt to sing the song of redeeming love?"

What is this song? Who sings it? Why? When is it sung? To whom is it sung?

During a vast missionary effort, the Prophet Alma in the Book of Mormon, asked of his brethren this important question, "...If ye have experienced a change of heart, and if ye have felt to sing the song of redeeming love, I would ask, can ye feel so now?" (Alma 5:26)

The prophet indicated that there must be a mighty change in the heart and this would allow the soul to expand, and when the soul expands and receives attendant promises, the person wants to sing!

NOTES

Singing can arise from within us for various reasons, but this particular song comes up from within our changed hearts, from our very depths, because of the power of God's word which is in us. Therefore, we have great reason to rejoice.

We believe in this redeeming, forgiving power of the Christ and in his word. Gradually we become aware of what love really is because we are becoming aware of what God's love has wrought for us, his children. The power of his atonement and the love we feel as his word teaches us, begin to consume our thoughts and our lives. The feeling of redeeming love appeals to our beings so richly we begin to emulate it, we want to be charitable and compassionate and to bring honor to the Lord.

With this influence in our lives we soon begin to experience the fruits of obedience to that word and from good labors. Our souls expand and when we are caught up in this great power to become his sons and daughters, rejoicing and praising often take the form of song within our souls.

NOTES

These are the reasons we sing the song of redeeming love. We feel we are forgiven and are on the right course. We have the power to remain on this course because repentance has been set in place through the mercy of the Lord. We have hope.

Well do I remember the occasions when I have gone to the top of the cemetery hill for my morning walks, and my heart was full to overflowing with thanksgiving to the Lord for his particular and multitudinous blessings. I had no adequate words to express my gratitude. There were none. There never are, it seems. Nothing I could have said simply or eloquently could possibly have told the Lord how I really felt or what great joy filled me--so I burst into song!

On those occasions I thought I almost knew how David of old must have felt when from within his soul he sang praises to the Lord. I created new melodies and lyrics, as David did in Bible days. They flowed from inspiration, led by the Holy Ghost, and were not necessarily burdened with forms and

NOTES

measures. I do not remember my songs now. They simply were outpourings of my spirit reaching toward heaven. And so rejoicing and praising became synonymous. What a wonderful feeling and powerful communion!

When Moroni wrote the last few words into the account left in his charge, he told how the repentant members of the Church were forgiven and then could expect their meetings to be led by the power of the Holy Ghost; "...for as the power of the Holy Ghost led them whether to preach, or to exhort, or to pray, or to supplicate, or to sing, even so it was done." (Moroni 6:9)

Have you ever stopped in the middle of teaching a class and asked class members to join you in prayer, or in a song because you were led by the spirit to so do? That can be managed with appropriate spontaneity.

Ammon said, "I do not boast in my own strength, nor in my own wisdom; but behold, my joy is full, yea, my heart is brim with joy, and I rejoice in

NOTES

my God." (Alma 26:10)

As any of us nearly perceive the greatness of the Lord, or begin to recognize the magnitude of his gifts to us, through grace and the redemption of our souls, we feel the urgent need to say thank you to him.

I remember once feeling, not irreverently, as if I wanted to throw my arms around the Lord and give him a big hug. I loved him so very much. We were struggling financially to rear our family and do the Lord's bidding, but somehow got behind in paying tithes. A few months rolled on, and my fears were that my husband had not the faith to do what he knew needed to be done.

My prayers heightened that he might be able to do what I knew he really wanted to do, pay the tithes at any cost. Very shortly, in the mail came a tax return in the exact amount we owed. My husband did not quibble or hesitate. He said, "I think we should pay our tithing." Our prayers were answered.

Praise and thanksgiving can fill to overflowing

NOTES

and so we often do as have others; we lift up our voices, somehow, to let escape the overwhelming desire to show our gratitude. Ungrateful hearts will never sing this song or know this joyful experience; not until repentance takes hold.

Isaiah foretold the joy to be felt when the watchmen "lift up the voice; with voice together shall they sing, for they shall see eye to eye when the Lord shall bring again Zion. Break forth into joy, sing together, ye waste places of Jerusalem; for the Lord hath comforted his people, he hath redeemed Jerusalem." (3 Nephi 16:18)

The brother of Jared sang praises unto the Lord, and he did thank and praise the Lord all the day long. When the night came, they did not cease to praise the Lord, because he had brought them, a believing, repentant, obedient body of Jaredites, safely over the ocean to the promised land.

Do we remember that it was through the principles spoken of that the brother of Jared and Isaiah came to a knowledge of their Redeemer? It

NOTES

was in this knowledge that they rejoiced, that their joy was full, that they saw fulfillment in the promises of the Lord.

Forgiving of sins, redemption of the righteous, seeing eye to eye with the judgment of the Lord opens the flood gates of thanksgiving, of praise and rejoicing.

Commandment is given to the heavens and the earth to "Sing, O heavens; and be joyful, O earth; and break forth into singing, O mountains; for the Lord hath comforted his people, and will have mercy upon his afflicted." (Isaiah 49:13)

When David realized the Lord blessed the earth, the crops, the flocks, he said they shouted for joy, "...they also sing." He suggested they "make a joyful noise unto God, all ye lands: Sing forth the honor of his name: make his praise glorious."
"In the transgression of an evil man there is a snare: but the righteous doth sing and rejoice." (Proverbs 29:6)

Israel, (and we too are the House of Israel) was

NOTES

commanded to sing praises to the Lord, and if ancient Israel had walked in the Lord's ways they would have triumphed over their enemies. They were told to "sing unto the Lord with the harp,...and the voice of a psalm. With trumpets and sound of cornet make a joyful noise before the Lord, the king."

Jehoshaphat appointed singers unto the Lord, that they should praise him as they went out before the army, and when they began to sing and to praise, the Lord set ambushments against the armies which came up against Judah, and they were smitten. (2 Chronicles 20:20-22)

King David taught us how to sing praises. He said, "Give thanks unto the Lord, call upon his name, make known his deeds among the people. Sing unto him, sing psalms unto him, talk ye of all his wondrous works." Again he said, "Serve the Lord with gladness, all ye his people--Be thankful unto him and bless his name. ...Make a joyful noise unto the Lord, all ye lands.

"...Enter into his gates with thanksgiving, and

NOTES

into his courts with praise: be thankful unto him, and bless his name. For the Lord is good: his mercy is everlasting; and his truth endureth to all generations. ...for praise is comely for the upright... ."

David taught of God's mercy and judgment in his songs and made promises to the Lord. He said he would forsake the company of evildoers; said he would behave himself wisely in a perfect way, that he would set no wicked thing before his eyes, that he "hated the work of them that turn aside and it would not cleave unto him."

But we have to keep in mind the warning given by Alma in his great discourse to his brethren to forever be repentant, be stripped of pride, be humble, be concerned about the poor, render service willingly in order that we can "feel to sing the song of redeeming love."

I am sure we may carry a song silently in our hearts as we do with a prayer, and we may have uncultivated voices with which to beautifully render songs. When we are asked to sing in our services

NOTES

unto the Lord, we might ask ourselves if our hearts are full enough of gratitude to make us lift our voices and sing with all our hearts? The Lord is interested in the condition of our hearts.

Our hymnal has many beautiful songs of praise, of thanksgiving, and supplication, showing our desire to have his spirit be with us always. The lyrics to numerous songs are found within the scriptures. One is found in the Doctrine and Covenants, Section 84:99-102. The Lord told us that a song of the heart delighteth his soul. He added that "the song of the righteous is a prayer" unto him that will be answered upon our heads with blessings.

Are we not also touched with heartfelt messages? Can we feel to sing songs of redeeming love to our Saviour and King? Saints filled with this kind of joy will have no difficulty in keeping the commandment to sing in gatherings meant to reverence the Lord.

The morning stars sang together in anticipation of the great plan of life and salvation being

NOTES

implemented on the earth, and a host of angels sang from the heavens on that spring night over the Shepherd's field in anticipation of the joy the world would know at the birth of the Christ child. Let us ponder what it may be like to "sing ceaseless praises with the choirs above, unto the Father, and unto the Son, and unto the Holy Ghost, which are one God, in a state of happiness which hath no end." (Mormon 7:7)

When the Lord shall stand upon Mount Zion and upon the holy city, the New Jerusalem, they, the resurrected righteous shall sing the song of the Lamb day and night forever and ever with all worthy sons and daughters of our Redeemer. What a joy it would be to be counted among those who will join in singing the songs of redeeming love at his coming. (D&C 128:23)

NOTES

****

Suggested Exercise

1. Our greatest spiritual blessings are perhaps better kept to ourselves because of their sacredness. If you have a special experience that you feel could be appropriately shared, would you tell about it? Parents can often share gifts or experiences with believing children, that indeed help to build their faith or reaffirm confidence in their own gifts.

NOTES

ALEX

Alex was a seven year old, the youngest of twelve children in the Cordner family in Pleasant Grove. He was learning to communicate effectively. Even though desperation spirited the encounter, Alex made the effort to do as he had been taught.

Alex's father raised his voice at him, so he went to his mother and told her! "What do you want to do about it?" she asked.

"We need a family council."

"You are welcome to ask Dad if he is free," she replied.

In a few minutes here came Alex holding his Dad by the hand and they sat on the bed. Alex respectfully began with his mother.

NOTES

"Mom, you're sending me to my room too easily. I'm not doing anything that bad. And Dad, if I yelled at you the way you just did, I would be sent to my room."

Then Alex went to get the only two older sisters that were home, and proceeded to tell them what they were doing unjustly to him.

One sister put her hand to her mouth, snickered and admitted, "Mom, he is right! I do that all the time, he is right!" She laughed and was amazed at Alex's calm but deliberate manner. The complaint, given in a sober but not hateful way, helped her to realize that she was being offensive.

The other sister stood right up and disagreed with his charges, "I'm not going to listen to this--!" And she was gone!

Then Alex asked the others in the room, "Do you have anything to say?"

Mom apologized and said she would be more careful about what she sent him to his room for, thereafter.

NOTES

Dad, dumbstruck, chagrined and amazed, sat on the bed very proud of this young son, and put his arm around his shoulders. Parents make mistakes too at times.

Alex continued. "Is there anything I've done you need to talk with me about?"

Mom said, "Not that I can think about right now--"

To which Alex insisted, "Surely there is something."

"No, none that I don't think you are already working on with Heavenly Father."

Alex had been heard. He had been fair and honest, and he was learning early in life to settle differences without yelling or hurtful accusations, but by developing skills that would endear him to his family and to others for years to come.

Trying to do the right thing in the right spirit, with love and not hate or disgust or impatience is what it takes to bring about desired needs for a troublesome atmosphere. Learn to be direct, to

NOTES

speak softly, and without an accusing whine is communication at its best. A prayerful approach will assist every time no matter how young you are.

****

Suggested Exercise

Q. Have you prayerfully approached a person or persons in your family with whom you have had difficulty and tried to talk things over?
Q. How did it turn out?

For additional help read the story called THE TEN ACRE PRINCIPLE in this volume.

Draw a picture about this story here, or to build comprehension, write your version of the story on this page.

Where several children are using one book, have them draw a picture or write their story and put their best work in their journals.

NOTES

STRAIGHT AS AN ARROW

A Scout, in any day or time, works with a conscious effort to be ready to enjoy--really enjoy--every adventure in Scouting! It just flows naturally with Scouting to develop skills, great health codes, reverence, and a positive attitude. A camping or hiking adventure can fizzle with a few on-going gripes and complaints. On the other hand, an activity can be great when there is a cooperative spirit, and each person pitches in to carry his share of the load.

I well remember one Scout who definitely got into the spirit of adventure by preparing for Scout Camp at Maple Dell, out in the Utah National Parks Council. He had a paper route and earned his own

NOTES

money for camp.

You see, once in a while he asked Mom to do his route for some reason or another, and wasn't always on top of his chores; (you know, Mr. Procrastination and short term memory!)

Now, all of a sudden, his mother began to notice just a few weeks before camp, Nathaniel, or Nat to his friends, had become exceptionally well organized. He was down to breakfast on time, without having to be called! He ate things he had not particularly relished before. In fact, he even asked for fruit for breakfast, and ate any vegetable his Mom put before him! Wow! The age of miracles had not passed!

More amazing was his subtle announcements, "I've already made my bed, Mom." Or proudly, "After my route, Mom, I'll have the lawn mowed by 5:30."

Nat kept his word. This routine of early sleep, eating good food, getting chores and extras done--on time, was great, but puzzling. Surely this would pass, thought his Mom, but it didn't.

NOTES

The family was in whispers, "What's going on with Nat? What's he up to?"

Boy! This change was great! Nat's dad decided further commendation was definitely in order. Besides, curiosity was getting the best of the family.

"Son, this new schedule is wonderful. You must feel really good about yourself these days. How do you do all this?"

Nat admitted that he wanted to get his money's worth out of camping this year! He wanted to have fun. "Last year, I had a bellyache half the time. I missed fishing two days, didn't feel like hiking, and was miserable sitting in the amphitheater during the awards night. Cory said I was a complainer and didn't want to do anything. This year I am going to be in shape. I am going to enjoy myself and everybody else."

Nat shook his head. "No more misery. I know I can bring in as many skill awards and fish as anyone, maybe more. But, Dad, you have to plan on things. I just decided I'd get in shape early. You

NOTES

started shaping up six months before our Fifty-miler."

Nat's dad had further thoughts, "My son is getting in shape in more ways than he can imagine! He is getting "the message". He is being true to himself. Being straight as an arrow mentally, physically and spiritually is what it is all about! He'll have a good time this year."

As he descended the stairs, Nat's Dad smiled to himself, "He is taking charge of his own life. I believe he knows what he wants and how to get it. You never know when a boy is going to really take charge of himself, I suppose."

NOTES

TAKING CHARGE

If the reason for taking charge,
Completely unto self,
Is to being about some order
In pursuit of happiness,
The struggles and the pain
Will begin to satisfy
Only if taking charge
Has taken on the task
Of giving unto others
What the heart is wont to ask.

Service unto others
Results in happiness,
Turns selfish thoughts and focus
To surprising happenstance.
For seeing bright eyes glowing
And hearts responding true
To love and to devotion
Brings warmth to your heart too.
What else is genuine joy,
Than seeing all go well?
'Tis not the hurt and tatters
Of self centerness pell-mell.

Draw a picture about this story here, or to build comprehension, write your version of the story on this page.

Where several children are using one book, have them draw a picture or write their story and put their best work in their journals.

NOTES

RULES THAT I SHALL BE GOVERNED BY

Boys go to scout camp for all kinds of reasons. Occasionally they go because someone else wants them to go--or to get away from the wrong crowd for a while. But you know, "the bad guys" show up anywhere! It isn't unheard of that boys with bad habits, bad attitudes go to camp too. They usually do not last long, or last happily until they catch the spirit of Scouting.

What does a person do to draw the line when around those people with bad attitudes, or habits, begin to foul up the works at school, camp, or even in the family?

I remember reading what a person did when faced with a challenge like this. It was during pioneer

NOTES

days. Chrest was not eighteen yet, but saw the opportunity to make some much needed money for his family by hiring on as a freighter with a freighting company.

Chrest realized freighting was a tough life and he would be around some pretty rough characters. Chrest also knew that making choices and planning ahead, what you would say and do, would help protect you. Values that help make your dreams come true never become obsolete. They are always good. They always work. And if a few stumbling blocks come along, a person is able to cope, to handle them better when their plans are already in place.

Surprises or circumstances are less likely to throw you if you are prepared. Handling difficult times then become only "growing pains", when you are prepared. And boys can handle growing pains. They have them all the time.

Chrest Petersen had survived a migration over the western plains and Rocky Mountains of America

NOTES

when Utah, Idaho, Nevada, and Arizona were being settled in the mid 1800s. His family had settled in Bear River City in northern Utah. They were struggling to make ends meet, to pull crops through for an oncoming winter. There was need for a good freight line to succeed in transporting supplies in to and out of the mountainous areas. So Chrest thought he would help that happen.

Chrest had grown physically and in "prairie smarts" and decided to accept a job as a freighter. He knew the dangers that beset a freighter. They get caught in all kinds of dangerous weather, run into problems of wagons and equipment breaking down while in remote areas. The terrain itself could be very hazardous, not to speak of the outlaws, the unruly characters who drank, swore, stole, and took advantage of people. But Chrest had not traveled with a two-wheel handcart over hundreds of miles in the heat and cold, pulling and pushing a four-by-six-foot handcart loaded with family essentials, to allow anyone to "do him in" now! So Chrest made some

NOTES

wise decisions, ahead of time, to assist himself in making the safest and smartest survival while earning wages to help his family.

Found in his old account book of September 1877 was this entry:

"Rules that I shall be governed by while freighting. First: I shall not take the name of the Lord in vain if tempted ever so badly. Second: When in company with bad men, I shall say but little and watch that they get no influence over me in any shape. Third: When insulted by a bad man, it is my duty to not say anything that will create more anger. It shall be my duty first, if these 3 rules cannot be kept by me, I shall quit freighting and go where I can keep them, Signed, Chrest Petersen."

Chrest had done some sound thinking. He set his own rules to live by. He wanted nothing to do with anything that could not contribute to making his dreams come true. And he had dreams! He wanted to help build a new home in the west where there could be industry and freedom. He wanted to be

NOTES

straight and honest so his friends and family could trust him and count on him in their dealings with him.

****

Suggested Exercise

Scouting principles expose boys to possible vocations. In troop activities, at camp, and at Merit Badge Pow Wows, opportunities abound for thinking ahead and practicing the rules you have set for yourself. Your example will communicate to others that you are smarter than the average bear! So go for it!

1. Decide now what your rules are going to be for governing yourself, and stick by them.

Write them in your journal for safe keeping. Read them often.

Draw a picture about this story here, or to build comprehension, write your version of the story on this page.

Where several children are using one book, have them draw a picture or write their story and put their best work in their journals.

NOTES

LITTLE OLD LADIES

I love little old ladies! I dearly love them.

I am sure this love began with my grand-mother, Mamaw Bales in Texas, who showed me that carrots were sweeter than candy, and true friends had no age, not really.

This love was reflected when my husband took our family to Philmont Scout Ranch in New Mexico years ago. The leaders were being trained in scouting skills, the children were being tended, and the ladies were taken to do crafts.

While everyone else made ash trays out of the handful of clay we were given, I sculpted a little old Relief Society President's head. Her little Sunday hat, her wrinkles and smile, her bun of hair at the

NOTES

back of her head above the high, lace trimmed collar with a cameo under her chin revealed my heart-and-soul love for her. I had never held clay in my hands before, but she did me proud!

Little old ladies represent to me many things. Little, only because even tall frames shorten eventually, and old because years have given them deep wells of learning from experiences you and I have yet to follow, some of which our maps were not designed to know. Yet the terrain they have covered in life make them what they are--wonderful!

The Prophet Joseph did not say we should learn to rejoice in the trials of others, only our own. When I see goodness exuding from those wrinkled brows and laughter-drawn crows feet at the eyes, I do rejoice in their triumphs, and yearn to listen, to learn.

You may remember one of my favorite Little Old Ladies. She was Swiss born, ninety-nine year old "Little Emma" Meyer who sat quietly in a nursing home where I taught Seminary and spent hours

NOTES

several days a week for a number of years after our children were grown.

I was told Emma was deaf, mute, extremely retarded and was placed in the nursing home after having spent about forty years in the state mental hospital--only because her parents had died and left her alone with an unruly, younger brother.

Emma was devastated. She had never lived with anyone else, was unable to communicate sufficiently. Finally a doctor said Emma did not need to be in the hospital. She only needed a home-like atmosphere and she was placed in a nursing home, but for twelve years no family members had come to visit Emma.

I was given permission to research Emma's background and to see if truly she had outgrown her relatives. We found that she had been born in Zurich, Switzerland and had come to the United States with the rest of her family when she was nineteen. Her father was a Zurich policeman, and upon retiring from police work, they came to the Salt

NOTES

Lake Valley and the whole family received their endowments and was sealed in the Logan Temple.

I found that well-behaved, modest Little Emma with the golden but toothless smile, turned at the sound of my voice and sometimes became tearful at a sensitive point in the lesson. Investigation revealed that Emma was born severely tongue tied and diagnosed to be less than she was! Deafness was incident to age.

Emma came alive when we began talking with her about her family! Emma expressed utter astonishment, nodded yes, and cried when I asked, "Was your mother's name Anna Maria Dietiker? Was your father Abraham?" It was so good to hear their names.

We brought music and pictures to see if we could make further breakthroughs to Emma. To our great surprise and pure delight, Emma "mouthed" the entire first verse of an old Swiss Folk Song we played for her on tape! She recognized nineteenth century landmarks from large pictures we showed

NOTES

her. How could an extremely retarded individual respond in the various ways she did if she were not recognizing and thinking to make choices, and remembering incidents of earlier life?

Another volunteer at the nursing home remembered that Emma had "yah, yah, yahed", tilted her head and kept rhythm to music she had played on her accordion to the residents.

We asked what she was playing when Emma did this. "Oh, just an old Swiss Folk Song!"

Once while I was teaching about some of the Saints going up the Mississippi River on a barge to conference, it reminded me of a story I was told by a nephew to Emma. I interrupted the lesson, went to Emma's side and knelt to be on her eye level and asked, "Emma, do you remember when your two sisters came ahead of the family to America with a few families and some missionaries?"

Surprised by my knowledge of the incident, Emma, nevertheless nodded yes. Then I asked, "Do you remember that everyone aboard ship got sea

NOTES

sick but your sisters?"

Emma threw back her head and guffawed! Her little frame shook with laughter at the remembrance.

The highlight of my experiences with Emma was when Emma wrote her name in long hand! I put her photograph on Christmas cards she could give away, wrote a brief note for her because of her painfully arthritic fingers, then asked if she would sign her name. It was not known whether she could write at all. The pride and ease with which she undertook the task brought tears to my eyes. Emma could write her name! "Miss Emma Meyer" was written clearly and beautifully.

Nina Hansen, President of the Relief Society for the nursing home, knelt at Emma's feet and offered a prayer for and in her behalf. Emma took Nina's hands and kissed them, kissed her arms and cheeks because she had been sensitive enough to know that Emma was a person, not a fixture, and may have yearned to "say" a prayer.

Emma died five weeks short of her one-hun-

NOTES

dred-fourth birthday, and is buried near her home in Providence, Utah. Emma's having come to this earth was hailed by the president of the United States, her beloved Prophet and General Relief Society president, many Wards, and congressional dignitaries. Whole Sunday School classes, and Tiny Tots came to give her hugs and performances. They sent stacks of cards and made many visits. (Emma's complete story is found in THE SONG OF A VOLUNTEER by Polly Block.)

I love another little old lady. While doing research for my first book in 1978, I was looking for stories about pioneer midwives. I learned of Anna Christina Peterson from Denmark. She died of cholera as an infant on the plains and because of Indians, time could not be taken to dig a grave. She had to be left wrapped in a blanket under a bush as her mother had been instructed.

Full of consternation, her mother, a "little old Relief Society lady", earning her gray hair and the jewels for her crown on this westward trek, went

NOTES

back during the following night. She went alone, despite the big prairie wolves that always followed the wagons and handcarts at a distance, and Indians, to retrieve her baby's body.

The next morning she was missed and while searching they found her stumbling wearily into camp with her precious burden. It was immediately discovered that "Annie" was alive!

Annie lived to finish the trek with her family who settled in Cedar Fort. At age sixteen Annie became the second wife to Samuel A. Wilcox, and a midwife who delivered over two hundred babies in Cedar Valley. She had six children of her own and also has become one of the most famous pioneer children in Mormon history.

Anna Christina Peterson Wilcox and her mother, Maren, both buried on the little cemetery hill at Cedar Fort, Utah, are role models for us in BENEATH A PRAIRIE BUSH, the first volume in a pioneer series called NURTURING THE SPIRIT. I do love Grandma Annie.

NOTES

One spring day we erected a modest plaque and rededicated Annie's grave site. This deliberately honored Maren for returning to get Annie, but we also honored Annie for the contributions she made under the primitive circumstances of those days in Cedar Valley.

My eleven-year-old granddaughter drove out to Cedar Fort with me one day in Grandpa's little pickup truck. We had the lawn mower. She had helped to restore the site because there was no perpetual care. I wanted Bridget to learn the joy of loving and serving. On the way home I looked into the sky above the steering wheel, and pretending, drew in a quick breath, reached into the air, caught something in my hand, and planted it on Bridget's cheek!

"Wow! There's a kiss from Grandma Annie Wilcox, Bridget! She knows you have worked hard all summer to keep her gravesite pretty. She blew that kiss to say thanks."

"Ahh, Grandma." Bridget grinned shyly.

NOTES

"Oh, it is true. She knows. She appreciates your keeping a pretty place from which to resurrect." We chuckled but I don't think Bridget will ever forget that summer when she too learned to love little old ladies.

To all little old ladies in the world who have brought joy, wisdom and support to their families and communities, and particularly to those who have come to live on earth without much notice, we notice. We salute you, we need you. We love you.

****

Suggested Exercises

Q. We communicate with body language, with words we speak, with acts of kindness. What did this story tell you?

Q. What do you like about older people?

Q. How many close, older friends do you have?

Q. What important things did your older friend do when he was younger? Was he or she a pioneer in some way?

What is one of the greatest things he or she could have done in life? (Be a faithful church member, a parent, a teacher, a builder, etc.)

NOTES

WHAT DOES IT TAKE?

Oh Mama, I'd like a cake!
What does it take, dear, to make a cake?
Oh Mama, lots o' sugar, it tastes so sweet.
Must take more, dear, that's a treat!
Can't guess, Mama, but you should know,
You've made beautiful ones to show.

Yes, my dear, but I had to learn
Without what it takes, it will fall and burn.

Oh Mama, I'd like a marriage!
What does it take, dear, to make a marriage?
Lots of loving, Mama, it's so sweet!
Must take more, dear, to be complete.
You should know, Mama, but please tarry,
What else is there to a marriage?

NOTES

Oh my child, let's understand
It takes commitment to wear a band;
And knowing needs, not just desires,
A little running through the fires
Are necessary to build patience and faith,
Else blindness obscures
Your need for God's grace.

Feel the pride of integrity,
The mentality of being fair,
A lot of giving before you take,
Then my child, make no mistake,
A steady marriage can be yours,
When laughter and fun gently lure
The sweetness of lots o' loving.

Communication Through Acts of Kindness

NOTES

OLD FASHION DIAMOND DUST

In a world where trends mold and bend,
There is a quality not forgot!
It is found in some whose life has begun
To spread lots of diamond dust.
Modesty, honesty,
Caring and sharing,
Kindness to the timid,
Courage and truth
Are not uncouth
But brighten a person's image.

When a heart full of giggles,
Boldly delivers
The giving of service with gust,
A person's sweet charity
Is bursting with clarity
To be full of diamond dust.

NOTES

PAYDAYS

It definitely became a payday when Keith, Annie, Ryan and B.J. did what they did! What's this all about, you ask? It is simple.

Just about everything parents do in life is done for their children. Stretching the budget, sacrificing, twenty-four hour vigilance, nurturing, teaching, setting examples, being a taxi, kissing mashed fingers well, working extra jobs to provide roofs overhead, food and raiment--it is all done willingly and out of love.

All that parents ask in return is that their children love the Lord, serve Him, and be honest in all their dealings. That covers more than you would think! When children do these things, it definitely

NOTES

becomes a payday to parents and to grandparents and makes a difference in the lives of others.

Mr. Keith Grover teaches in a Spanish Immersion program in Meadow Elementary School in Lehi, Utah. He came from teaching disadvantaged Tarahumara Indian children in Chihuahua, Mexico where they had no crayons, no chalk, no desks, no school lunches, only the crude slates of yesteryear with which to learn.

Mr. Grover had the children's bright eyed, undivided attention and their love for learning but only his knowledge and love as teaching tools.

In and around Lehi, school children and neighbors got together and amassed an abundance of school supplies, books, clothing and sewing needles, scissors, cloth dolls, simple string games, etc. for Mr. Grover to take to the Tarahumara Indian children on his yearly visit to them.

Today Mr. Grover uses those same skills to reach the inner light of the children in Lehi's Spanish program, and teach he does!

NOTES

Mr. Grover's students "have so much fun they don't know they are learning," he says.

One student from a broken home with heart-aches for three years is now one of Mr. Grover's happiest students. Annie smiles all the time, and came home with straight A's. The difference in Annie is certainly a happy payday for Annie and for her Mom.

Though a grown person, and going on with his life, Mr. Grover continues to do compassionate service to the remote Tarahumara and other children he has learned to love. What paydays Mr. Grover has given his adoptive mother, Kay, who sees his on-going commitment to those in need!

Ryan, a thirteen year old Junior High student in Pleasant Grove, Utah also gave his parents and Grandma a payday when instead of wasting away time, or "hanging out" with his friends all the time, he wrote a song, and penciled some very good sketches.

When his Mom encouraged him to answer the

NOTES

call for an illustrator for a children's book, he did, even though he was only a young boy! He got the job and drew the cover and twenty-one illustrations for the book.

Becoming a published illustrator at age thirteen was a great payday. (The children's book Ryan illustrated is *THE FASTEST BUGGY HORSE IN ALPINE,* by Polly Block.)

B.J. is a student in American Fork High School who works hard to maintain a 4.0 average in spite of the fact that he sings in the concert chorale, is the third best runner in his gym class, and has a paper route after school. B.J. usually has little children around him because he pays attention to them instead of brushing them aside as "little kids".

B.J. is very goal oriented and once a goal is set he works hard at it. His heart is set on being a pediatrician.

His mother says B.J. is "into mind moods", that he is very much aware of other peoples' feelings and moods. B.J.'s countenance reveals a clean and

NOTES

outgoing person who would certainly have his mind on such things. When his mother is down in the dumps, she can always count on B.J. to put his arm around her and tell her how much he appreciates her.

He is the peacemaker among his three brothers and a sister. He doesn't speak of his own accomplishments, but his communication skills go beyond the use of words. Wouldn't you say that a person with this focus in life would continue to bring home paydays to his family?

****

Suggested Exercise

Q. You are a good person. Reading this book with hopes of learning how to communicate better is really something to give as a Payday.

Will you practice all you have learned and set an example to your family?

Q. Let me put a secret in your cap: One of the BIGGEST PAYDAYS for a teacher is to have a student glue his eyes to her eyes when she is talking to him. Another is to have a student get really excited about learning! It makes her feel as though she is teaching right and you are really learning!

NOTES

WHAT'S IN A NAME?

Do you like your name? We all have to have one. Everyone has some kind of identification, a title or designation. Cowboys used to call your name a "handle".

Name giving inevitably reveals the nature of the giver. Some desire to give completely original or concocted combinations. Others show tremendous pride in family and in political and religious heritages. This becomes apparent when you have an overview of millions of names before you as we did a few years ago.

The first year in the Original Data Entry Program of the Church of Jesus Christ of Latter-day Saints brought delightful tickles throughout our days and nights. We entered four-plus generation

NOTES

information into the genealogy computer files while working in the program. The records dealt with family names from 1700 through the late 1900.

Even today traditional Given and Sir names are interwoven down through the generations of families. Our interests soared when we found unusual combinations of given names in the records.

One child naming trend found in the material gave ordinary names to the first few children, followed by at least four beautiful, many syllable names to the next few. For example one child might have been named Mathilda Theresa Lovinia Susannah Smith! Perhaps the mother thought she may never have another child, so she had better use all the pretty names she could think of on this one!

A few parents may have had over active senses of humor--and their children, I hope, shared the humor or they perished! I loved Experienced Pain, Olive Branch, Icie Bell, Bluebell Dazey, Miles Wise, Poor Jones, and Missouri Jane. Pinkie's last name was Cheek! These were actual first and last

NOTES

names of individuals listed in public records.

Often a second or third child received an identical name formerly given to one or more offspring in the family who had died. I wondered why? Then I smiled as I thought into the future; in the Great Beyond three individuals in the *same families* are going to answer to the *same* name when called! Will there be confusion or what?

Sometimes parents had twelve or fourteen children--which was not uncommon in earlier generations. So many times we found that the first eight or ten were given multiple, illustrious, dignified, patriotic, just-right sounding names that musically rolled off the tongue. The last four or five children had to be content--or relieved--with one short, good old standby such as Bertie, Ned, Earl, or Minnie.

The names which brought more chuckles to our silent, busy computer room were some of the following: Sarah Felt Little, Carrie Ake, Mable May Call, Bill Piggs, Grace Piggs, Peter Later, Pinky Card, Garnet Dinges, Oscar Meyer (we all know and

NOTES

love this one), Dewey Beach, Horace Peter, and Mary Chicken Farley.

We felt no desire to make fun of these poor little souls who had no choice of what their names would be, but our emotions were touched in various ways.

We listed the following under child abuse: Oder Smelley, his sister Oma Smelley that married Dink Lamdram. Other unusual names were Marion Rose Bush, Hugh Job Dunn, Willie Ophelia Reynolds, Ira Green Glase, Rural Pearl, Clinking Beard and even Jack Frost.

The next one had us all stumped as to how to pronounce it. Only twenty-two letters in one of those beautiful Hawaiian names, Lehauaonapaliokekoolaw. We thought maybe "hey you"!

My empathy truly wrapped around some children and their parents who had novel last names. I wondered what torment, bewilderment, or down right daring went into the following decisions? The girls

NOTES

were called Content Wetmore, Patience Wetmore, Meritable Wetmore, and Comfort Wetmore. I pondered over what I would have done with that Sir-name. Those who passed on family names were proud to do so, but some names must have brought perplexity somewhere along the line.

A big baby boy from one of my own ancestral families was named Pouncie Knuckols Pedigo!

As circumstances follow Cupid around in life, we see couples with humorous names marrying. Jolley-Day, Jolley-Wolfe, Jolley-Grubbs, Brown-Day, Day-Walker. How about these: Sapp-Farmer, Stiff-Sexton, Increase Child married Olive Peas, Too-Fort, Litle-Large, Large-Girth, Litle-Long, Litle-Wolfe, Litle-Hall, and Richard Money married Eliza Banks.

Families duly influenced by Church leaders named boys Orson, Hyrum, Parley, Brigham, or Joseph. One son was labeled Joseph Mormon Harris.

A few tears dropped from my cheek when I typed information relating to some places of death or

NOTES

burial such as "died crossing the plains" or "buried at sea in the North Atlantic".

There was magic in the names of exotic places of origin. New localities to me were Rising City, Fountain Green, Meadows of Dan, Blue Earth, Pipestone Creek, and Summer Shade, to name just a few.

The names most often given girls were Elizabeth and Marie (different forms of Mary), and boys were most often named some form of William, John, George and Frederick.

Fanny Pew, Jerusha Golden Glove, Mercyetta, Americus and Pleasant Whitlow join me in contemplating what earthshaking and life molding influences the names you choose for your children will inevitably have. Do you like the name you were given now?

NOTES

****

Suggest Exercise

Q. What would you do if you knew someone with a peculiar name?

Q. If your name is very different and people sometimes laugh, how do you handle that?

Q. Have you ever stopped others from making fun of another person? How did you do it?

Q. Does it take a lot of courage to defend another's good name? Is there a tactful, nice way to do this? Tell what you could do or say.

NOTES

ON THE OTHER HAND

ON THE OTHER HAND, as the leading character in Fiddler On The Roof would say, a good name is better than precious ointment and rather to be chosen than great riches.

The playful look at our names in the previous story is just that, a humorous observation. There is a sober side to this practice of naming people and things. Those who love us gave us our names. In a sense names become a badge of honor, of love.

If you are not terribly happy with the name you have, get busy and do something outstanding for mankind, and it will be changed!

The Savior had many names. As He performed a valiant service or mission He was given a new

NOTES

name from time to time. He was called Wonderful, Counselor, The Mighty One, The Christ and many others. See how many names you can find for the Savior as you read your scriptures.

So important are names that all things, trees, stars in the heavens, animals, mountains, valleys, cities, flowers--all things have been named. That is their individual, unique identification.

When Abram was renamed by the Lord, only the spelling was changed from Abram to Abraham, but the significance was great. Because of his righteousness his posterity would become as great in numbers as the grains of sand on the sea shores!

For instance, Isaiah said God shall call his servants by another name. What new name were we former gentiles given? We are called Mormons, Latter-day Saints, Christians, disciples. We are even called peculiar!

The whole family in heaven and earth is called disciples if they are true followers of Christ.

In Mosiah a whole nation of people had their

NOTES

names taken away. They were no longer called by the names of their wicked fathers! They chose to be called Nephites after those who were more righteous.

It tells us in Proverbs that the memory of the just (good) is blessed, but the name of the wicked shall rot! So we must keep trying to grow in righteousness if we want to be remembered.

We are told in the Doctrine and Covenants that if we are not willing to tithe and keep commandments our genealogies will not be kept or found on the records of the Church, or written in the book of the law of God.

The Lord loves his children. He is merciful and understands that we make mistakes. He forgives us as long as we don't give up, but keep trying to be as good as we can.

A fine example we can relate to is the story of President George Albert Smith. Before he became president of the Church he had a dream. In the dream his grandfather, for whom he was named,

NOTES

came to him and asked what he had done with his name?

George Albert Smith, in the dream as he stood before his grandfather, said his whole life flashed before his eyes, and finally he could say, to him, "I have never done a thing with your name for which you would be ashamed."

George Albert wept for hours during the rest of the night with thanksgiving that he was able to give his grandfather a good report instead of a blemished one.

We should all reverence the honorable names we have been given, and carry them with pride whether they are famous names, or just ordinary good names.

If by any chance the name we bear at the present has tarnish upon it, what an opportunity we have to bring some honor and glory to that name by our honest and honorable behavior all the days of our lives.

NOTES

****

Suggested Exercise

Q. Make a list of the names of your ancestors as far back as possible. How many of them had funny, patriotic, or made-up names? What were they?

Q. Do you have a nick-name? Sometimes nick-names become well known for accomplishments. "Mormon" is also a nick-name.

The following story is typical of positive thoughts and ingenious application of good communication. Notice the powerful touch it had on the lives of a whole city as well as many other people in the world.

NOTES

LAKE JACKSON'S WAY

"Tell your Mom and Valerie to have Aunt Kay bring all of you over to the hospital. You'd never find it alone. She will explain. See you later. Goodbye."

Aunt Kay had taken care of Gramps since Grandma had passed away. They lived down on the Gulf Coast of Texas and Gramps had been taken to a nearby town called Lake Jackson to the hospital.

"I guess I had to come to the hospital to have an operation before you would come to see me!" Grandfather teased on the telephone to Jimmy, even though the nurse was trying to put a thermometer in his mouth to hurry him off the phone.

"Gramps, are you all right?" Jimmy asked

NOTES

expecting the worse.

"Jimmy, the bad part is all over. I am going to be fine if you'll just come to see me.

Following lunch at Aunt Kay's, everyone got ready to go to the hospital in Lake Jackson to see Gramps.

Aunt Kay said, "Well, we had better be off, your Grandpa is waiting to see you."

As they neared the city of Lake Jackson Jimmy asked Aunt Kay, "Why did Gramps say we would never find the hospital? Don't you know how to get there?"

Aunt Kay answered, "Sure, but until you have been there a number of times you would get lost for sure. Remember this is Texas, not Utah, where the streets are numbered and organized in their unique way. Once you have caught on to the system, finding an address in Utah is easy. I'll tell you what, Jimmy, you and Valerie read all the street signs. I will go slowly, and you tell me how to get to the hospital. O.K.?"

NOTES

Aunt Kay handed the address to the children who immediately began to watch for the first street sign past the highway turnoff into the city of Lake Jackson.

Aunt Kay smiled, winked at their mother and quietly said, "A newcomer is apt to find himself just riding around the city looking at the street signs and squealing with delight at each new discovery. Let's see what the children do."

"There it is...it says THIS WAY! Turn right, Aunt Kay."

"But that takes you to that pretty church, not to the hospital...and look!" She pointed and said, "You'll miss the parking lot if you don't turn in on HIS WAY."

Aunt Kay listened for responses from the children.

"Look! The street sign into the parking lot does say HIS WAY!" The children began to laugh, "Oh, I see. The church is Heavenly Father's 'WAY'." They giggled some more.

Kay drove on down the street, and the children

NOTES

were watching closely. "Where are we now?" asked Aunt Kay.

"We're on WINDING WAY, and it sure is winding around. Here comes another street that says...ANY WAY! You've got to be kidding! These are the real names of the streets?" Jimmy shook his head in amazement. ANY WAY will get you there, huh?"

"Next street is...THAT WAY! THAT WAY? does that mean THAT is the way???" Valerie was rolling on the back seat holding her stomach with uncontrolled laughter.

They approached another intersection. They left ANY WAY street onto PARKING WAY. The children's mother said, "This sounds like the radio program of comedians Bud Abbott and Lou Costello giving a performance of 'Who is on First, and What is on Third', the baseball game mix-up!'

Next came CIRCLE WAY and GALLEY WAY. Aunt Kay said that was due to the influence of the Navy on the Gulf of Mexico. The street named

NOTES

CENTER WAY crossed ROBIN HOOD WAY and WARSAW WAY.

Jimmy asked, "What made them name the streets like this, Aunt Kay?" Humor and enthusiasm built while all eyes searched for succeeding street signs.

"Lake Jackson is inhabited by commuters to the big city of Houston. Professionals and VIPs no doubt find it refreshing to come home to a town that greets them with some lightheartedness reflected in the naming of their streets. Here is another part of town that is fun too. It is right on the way to the hospital. Watch these street names."

RABBIT TRAIL turned into TULIP TRAIL, BLUEBONNET CENTER, SPANISH MOSS, QUAIL RUN AND BUFFALO TRAIL...Jimmy wondered what it would be like to live on BUFFALO TRAIL!

"Oh, GREAT! Look at the next one: PIN MONEY! I'd like to live on PIN MONEY street," said Valerie. "I'd have pin money in my pockets all the time!"

NOTES

"Here comes WINE GLASS STREET and LAZY LANE, which naturally had to be followed by SLEEPY HOLLOW, and RIP VAN WINKLE streets."

"I cannot believe this is for real...just look!" Jimmy's mother was also amazed.

"How about CAYENNE COMMON? You know people in the south use lots of cayenne pepper in their cooking."

Aunt Kay was the best tour guide. She told so many interesting things about what they were seeing. "Some of these names reflect old practices in the south. As small communities developed, paths or trails often taken by the people or used by animals were named...like this one: FAWNS' WAY."

Remarkable events were remembered and often those landmarks were never changed, the trail was made into a legitimate roadway, but named for the event. The street that led down to the beach where driftwood piled high was named DRIFTWOOD Street.

"Coastal sites naturally provide ideas for street

NOTES

names. ANCHOR STREET, SURF SIDE, PIECES OF EIGHT--they are all here."

Jimmy interrupted to ask, "What's that?"

"Oh, pieces of eight were pieces of money used by pirates on the sea. Here is a street named DEMI-JOHN ISLAND, and there is CORAL DRIVE, SEASHELL and SANDOLLAR down that way. Do you know what a sandollar is, Valerie?"

Jimmy broke in proudly, "That's a small fish that looks like a silver dollar--look! there is EDGEWATER and BEACH DRIVE."

Jimmy squealed when he saw a street named for his favorite book, TREASURE ISLAND, and the names of scary fish like BARRACUDA! "This whole town has gone bananas!"

"We're here. Let's go see how Gramps is."

"What took you so long, Jimmy and Valerie? Did you lose you way? Did you get lost?"

Their mother kissed her father and remarked, "We couldn't believe this town and all those funny named streets!"

NOTES

Gramps asked, "Did you come by the flower streets?"

"No, Gramps, where are they?"

"Boy, on the street named MAGNOLIA, Jimmy, you will find lots and lots of those big old native southern trees with beautiful large, white magnolia blossoms. The whole street smells wonderful. And on the other flower streets it seems as if the people who live there have planted in their yards and around their walks just loads of the kind of flowers their street is named for--I never saw such as beautiful sight as I did on BACHELOR BUTTON street!"

This colorful town had really captured their interest. Gramps told them that down in Texas there were Gardenia bushes along streets and in yards just like your mother's favorite corsage flower.

The children looked up at their mother with a question on their faces.

The mother smiled at her dad and asked, "How did you remember that after all these years?" She kissed him on the cheek. "I used to wear a gardenia

NOTES

on my wrist to dances."

Gramps was cheered immensely by the visit of his grandchildren and his daughter. Even though he was in the hospital, Gramps had brought a lot of smiles and a very different adventure to them this trip to Texas.

"We're going to dream about sweet smelling streets and laugh about THIS and THAT AWAY directions instead of alligators and snakes all the time!" said Jimmy.

Valerie said on the return flight over Lake Jackson she thought she would write (communicate with) the Chamber of Commerce in Lake Jackson when she got home and tell them how much she liked their wonderful city of funny names.

Draw a picture about this story here, or to build comprehension, write your version of the story on this page.

Where several children are using one book, have them draw a picture or write their story and put their **best work in their journals.**

NOTES

ALLIGATORS ANYWAY!

Jimmy and Valerie found great fun and excitement each time they visited Gramps in Texas. They could hardly wait for the plane to touch down on the runway, yet they had to admit that their stays were sometimes scary enough to cause goose-pimples on their arms!

"Too bad Gramps is sick. He won't get to do things with us." Jimmy sighed.

Driving home from the airport Aunt Kay said,

"I thought you two would never want to come to see us after that last trip. Did you have nightmares about the snakes after you left?" Aunt Kay remembered their wide eyes and daily reactions to

NOTES

some of the adventures of their last trip.

Jimmy grinned and excitedly told Aunt Kay, "When I went to school and told the kids about those boys who went hunting with --what did you call them--those sacks--?"

"You mean the tow sacks. That is what we call gunny sacks in Texas. You tow or pull potatoes or rice in the sacks, Jimmy," explained Aunt Kay.

"Yeah, when I told them about the favorite pastime of the boys they said there weren't that many snakes in the world!"

"What did you tell them, Jimmy?" asked Valerie.

"Remember when we were in the dentist's waiting room? Those two teenagers came in and told a lady what they had been doing all morning." reminded Jimmy.

"Oh yes, they said they loved to take their twenty-two guns and tow sacks down into the rice fields and shoot rattle snakes."

Yuk!" answered Valerie, Jimmy's younger

NOTES

sister.

The boys had tow sacks half full of dead snakes they bragged about to everyone.

"Or was it water moccasins they shot, Aunt Kay?"

"Could have been either one, Jimmy. The fields are full of them, I'm afraid. They try to see who can get their sacks the fullest, but don't you go down there! The men who work in the fields only go down on their tractors to plant or to harvest," Aunt Kay warned them. "Some day those kids will get hurt."

When they arrived in Danbury, all went into the house on the fifteen foot mound of dirt Uncle Ray had built to avoid being flooded out during storms. Danbury was only six feet above sea level and about that many miles from the Gulf of Mexico.

They unpacked and was eating a snack when Valerie turned to answer a knock on the door. It was a neighbor boy who mowed Aunt Kay's lawn.

"Come quick and see what my dad found in the irrigation ditch this morning!"

NOTES

Aunt Kay asked what was so exciting? When the boy told her, Aunt Kay hesitated and said, "You kids are going to never want to come down here again!"

On second thought she added, "It really isn't that unusual, but y'all aren't used to this and we do have lots of fun and non-dangerous things to do in Texas. You'll think the only things that live here are snakes and alligators."

"Alligators! Again?" Jimmy dropped his fork! He immediately thought of last year's adventure.

"Remember those men who came to dig out the irrigation ditch last year? They found out that the big concrete pipe under the bridge was stopped up. They couldn't dig it out, so they lifted the big pipe up at one end and out slid a big, huge alligator! The men said he had gone in there and probably found enough to eat in the pipe so he just stayed there and grew until he was so big he couldn't get out!" Jimmy delighted in retelling the story.

Aunt Kay said, "They couldn't figure out why

NOTES

the water had slowed down and backed up so much until they investigated."

Jimmy hurried, "Let's go see what's up across the street."

They went across the street to see what all the excitement was about. Jimmy, Valerie, their mother, and Aunt Kay found a group of neighbors standing around--but not too close to a horse's drinking trough. They peeked on tiptoes to see something, then jumped back quickly.

As Jimmy approached the trough, someone grabbed his arm and would not let him get close. Instead a man lifted Jimmy up so he could observe without being in danger.

There in the trough lay an alligator about three feet long!

"Wow! Where'd you get that?" exclaimed Jimmy.

Valerie was lifted up so she too could see what looked like a big fat lizard.

She squealed, and the man handed her to her Mom.

NOTES

The alligator swished his tail and water splashed all over everyone and they scattered! He tried to climb out of the trough, but the men had nailed some chicken wire over the trough to keep him captive.

The neighbor answered Jimmy's question, "Oh, we found him over there in the ditch. We will turn him loose in a while."

Valerie noticed the hard, thick and rough skin on the alligator's back, and his short little legs, but his tail was as long as his body and it was very strong.

A teenage boy in the crowd said, "Those things swim by moving their tails back and forth and they can run thirty-five miles an hour on the ground when they want to."

Jimmy asked, "How old is he? He is a little one compared to the alligator they found under the bridge last year."

Someone answered, "I'spect he is three or four years old. Did you ever see a baby one? They are about like this--," the man demonstrated by holding

NOTES

his hands just a few inches apart. "but they can bite pretty fiercely even then. You don't want to mess with them."

Another observer said, "They don't exactly bite with those long jaws. They just clamp down on a small animal, such as a pig or a dog--or person with jaws that are just like a vice. Then they swim out into the water and hold their catch under until they drown so they can tear them apart to eat them later."

Aunt Kay hurried to say, "But they seldom attack human beings. Just stay away from them."

Valerie asked, "How many babies do their mothers have?"

The teenager spoke up, "They have a whole passel of 'em, about fifty little hard eggs. She makes a big, deep nest of grass in the swampy part of the fields. They like frogs and fish and snakes and sometimes eat turtles."

A man watching the captured alligator in the trough said, "The mothers don't grow very long though. Sometimes if they live long enough, they'll

NOTES

grow about six or eight feet, but the males are the ones that get big. Whew! I've seen them eleven or twelve feet long, and they weigh over four or five hundred pounds."

Jimmy said he thought the big one under the bridge last year must have been that fat! Then he wondered, "How old do you s'pose that big one was, Mister?"

"Well", he replied, "They can live about fifty or sixty years, I understand, Jimmy."

The boy who mowed lawns came with his dad and said it was time to let the alligator go. Talk about communication! The people standing around went faster! They didn't want to stand around and watch a confused and frightened alligator let loose.

Aunt Kay said, "Now you kids don't have bad dreams tonight."

Jimmy was so excited. He had begun to imagine the tale he would tell his classmates this year when they returned from vacationing in the most exciting place he knew!

Draw a picture about this story here, or to build comprehension, write your version of the story on this page.

Where several children are using one book, have them draw a picture or write their story and put their best work in their journals.

NOTES

THE TEN ACRE PRINCIPLE

"Did you hear what he said to the teacher? I could clobber him for spouting off like that." Mary was exasperated with Tom for again he was being obnoxious in class.

"I know, he embarrassed me to death in history last week. We ought to do something about this. I wish he wasn't even around this school. Frankly, he upsets me!"

Leon agreed with the group of students who were entering the hall on the way to lunch.

The group of six found a place to sit and share lunch as they always did. They were opening their sack lunches when the topic of Tom Petty came up again. They had just settled down when Sarah Lou

NOTES

put her sandwich down in her lap and slumped down in apparent despair.

"If Tom does one more ignorant thing I'm going to quit school!"

Everyone turned to Sarah Lou and slowly one after another began to make a plan to get rid of the bothersome and uncouth classmate, Tom. They were unwilling to allow Tom any more slack in his behavior.

"I'm not going to quit school!" Leon began to show spunk. "I like school here and I'm not going to let Tom Petty kick me out just because he hasn't grown up."

Hank observed their various attitudes, but just ate in silence. Larry Simms paid close attention to what was going on but wolfed down his lunch, also in silence. Adriann's slow simmer erupted with a chatter of ideas.

"We could boycott school unless Tom was expelled. That'd teach him. I'm tired of putting up with his antics. He's just plain stupid."

NOTES

There were two or three "yeahs" and Larry Simms suggested that the girls just leave it to the boys who would take Tom to the park and "take matters into our hands--we'll fix him so he won't ever mess up again."

Hank had finished his lunch by now and decided that it was time to say something.

"You're acting as crazy as Tom. That is not the way to handle something like this."

All eyes turned to Hank, the Senior. They usually expected something sober from him because he was two years older than the rest of his classmates, and was the articulate one at school!. They usually listened even if at first they disagreed.

"Didn't you know that nobody'll change if you put them down or push them into a corner?"

"Well, he deserves it, Hank. I can't stand this anymore!" Val, who had also been more interested in food, finally joined in, "We've got to do something. We have a good teacher but she won't be with us long if this keeps up!"

NOTES

All chimed in with, "What else can we do?"

Hank shoved his chair back and said, "I'll tell you if you really want to know--do you?"

"Sure." They agreed.

"Last night I heard about the neatest way to solve problems like this. My Mom and Dad went to this meeting, see? They were talking about this principle they called The Ten Acre Principle--and it goes right along with common sense, and the gospel too."

Hank cleared his throat and really got into the story. "See, when you start telling people what they are doing wrong--which is putting them down in a way--all their thinking and their energies go into their defense. They tell you why they are doing what they are doing, whose fault it is, and say 'besides it is none of your business anyhow!' Don't they?"

Heads nodded or shoulders shrugged, but they continued to listen to Hank as he went on.

"See, they get so worked up defending themselves they *don't hear a word you say! They don't*

NOTES

hear any of your good ideas about what they ought to be doing or why they shouldn't be doing all the ignorant things they are doing."

Eyes opened a little wider because this was the gospel truth--never in the past had Tom paid any attention to their complaints about his attitudes or behaviors.

Hank went on, "So what you do is apply The Ten Acre Principle." Hank drew a piece of paper out of his notebook as his dad had done the night before. With his pencil he began to divide the paper into three separate sections. He hoped he could remember the principle as he had heard it from his parents. Several of them leaned forward to watch Hank's illustration.

(It is suggested that class members follow the instructions Hank gives and fill in the sections with appropriate information on their own sheets of paper. This will make more indelible on their minds the concepts Hank explains.)

At the top of the column on the left write "Mine"

NOTES

for your own ten acres. In the column on the right write "Yours" for the other fellow's ten acres. Now in the middle section write "Our Three Acres". This is the space where you will write down all the things a family or classroom does together.

"Wait a minute, Hank, I vaguely remember hearing about this before and it is a good idea, but you know what?"

"What?" asked Hank.

It's time to go back to class and I think you should do this in front of the whole class for all of us and maybe it will be a kinder hint for Tom to shape up, and it will help us remember what our school stands for in the first place and that's learning how to live the gospel the right way."

Mary admitted they were a little impetuous about the whole thing, and this sounded promising.

Mary, Leon, Hank, Larry and Val entered the classroom and Sarah Lou was standing by the blackboard with their teacher explaining their request. Their conversation went on for a few

NOTES

minutes, then their teacher smiled and said she would monitor the lesson to make sure all went well. She turned over the class to Hank with these few words:

"I am pleased that some of you have come up with a solution to problems in everyday life. Please give your attention to Hank as he gives the lesson.

Hank started all over so the entire class would know what was going on. He did not mention anyone's name or problem. This was to be a general problem solving technique. When he got to the part where they needed to fill in the three divided sections on the blackboard, he called on members of the class to give examples of what the class did together, not separately, in their learning periods.

They mentioned that they read, or studied, or wrote, or verbally participated in exercises one way or another. They had fund raising projects, car-pooled, picnics, field trips, etc.

"How does that apply to families?" asked Hank?

NOTES

Everyone thought for a moment and hands began to raise.

"We go on vacations together."

"We cook together."

Sarah Lou added, "We each have our own jobs with yard work--"

Hank corrected, "Then YOUR part of the yard work becomes YOUR responsibility, and that is on YOUR ten acres! How you do it, when you do it is your ten acres. It will reflect on your character and how you perform on your own when people see how you work."

There was a mouthing acknowledgment "Ohhh" response in the class as they began to get the picture.

Hank, feeling the magic cloak of teacherhood, complimented them. "There, this class has no dummies. You are getting the picture already. But let's go on."

"Let's take an example. Say in your family that you are living the Ten Acre Principle. What is on

NOTES

Dad's ten acres? What totally is his responsibility?

Answers came.

"How he makes the living."

"What kind of car he buys."

"Whose turn at family prayers."

"What kind of clothes he wears," shouted out Leon who liked to wear clothes just a little far out!

"Leon, you are exactly right--" said Hank who was interrupted by Mary.

"Unless Mom can't stand them. Like my Dad wore this dirty shirt to the store one night with her. She was soooo embarrassed!"

"Mary, you have brought up the greatest point we have to consider. Thanks. Now hear this: WHAT IF SOMEONE ON HIS OWN TEN ACRES DOES SOMETHING THAT IS NONE OF YOUR BUSINESS, BUT YOU HAVE A REAL PROBLEM WITH IT? If someone is taking care of his own business, his own responsibility, do you have any right to "butt in" or try to change him?"

Larry said, "Sure, if it is bugging you, tell him to

NOTES

slack off."

Sarah Lou said, "I don't think so. Not if it is none of your business and it isn't hurting you or bothering your ten acres!"

"Good thinking, both of you. But here is how you handle that. You say to the offender, 'May I come onto your ten acres for a short talk?'" Hank took his chalk in hand and moved onto the right hand column.

"This says to him, 'I know what you are doing is on your turf, but I need to talk with you about what you are doing.'"

"That takes finger pointing, accusations, and personal put-downs out of the picture and lets the person keep his dignity, or helps him save face, as the saying goes. There is no reason to be offended or to call up defenses or excuses or anything. This is just a talk, and permission is being given!"

Hank worked hard to remember exactly as possible the concept he had heard his mother and father discussing the night before.

NOTES

Hank pointed his finger toward the class and said, "Be straight forward, but kind about your complaint and request. How could your mother tell your dad she wishes he would wear cleaner shirts to the store, Val?"

"Well, you could just say...uh, I know you really like that old blue work shirt, but I feel that people'll think I don't keep clean shirts ready for you...and you look cool when you are all cleaned up. Would you please wear fresh clothes when you go out?"

Everybody cheered aloud and clapped. Val had outdone himself!

Larry chimed in, "Or you could say 'Let Larry take the car down to the store for us!"

Everyone laughed and said, "Yeah, sure!" They knew Larry's Dad had a new four wheel drive Larry loved to get his hands on as often as possible!

"Now," spoke Hank, "Isn't Larry's dad apt to think about the effect of his appearance on his wife's feelings, and make him want to consider that polite request, even though choosing what to wear is on

NOTES

his ten acres?"

Larry became more serious and asked, "Yeah, but my folks wouldn't let me do just ANYTHING I wanted to do even if it is on my ten acres. What do you do then?"

Hank answered, "I asked my Dad that very question Larry. He said we needed to consider one other thing our family does all together--on that three acres where we plan together as a family."

"What do you mean?" asked Sarah Lou.

"Well, he says if we all want to go back to heaven as an eternal family, there are certain behaviors and activities, as a family, we should want to do to get there safely. We talked about that. Mom said if we all agreed to not get too far out with our clothes and hair styles, we'd ask the family to 'check it out' and take the counsel or guidance they could give--just when we had a new urge to go ballistic! After all, if we really want to do the right thing--and we all do--on our own ten acres, it is up to us to use our talents, our ideas and timing and still keep our

NOTES

commitments. That gives us plenty of freedom. We just have to remember that most of how we operate on our ten acres effects others in
some way at some point and time so we have to be considerate of others too."

Val volunteered, "That's fair if they give you a little leeway to use your agency about things."

"MY FOLKS WOULDN'T GIVE IN ANY!" Mary burst out freely.

Sarah Lou spoke up, "There! There is a good reason for asking to go onto their ten acres as a parent--to get a reasonable compromise! Besides, people are always telling us we need to communicate more with our parents. Maybe they would really listen to us if they thought we were going to get on their ten acres!"

Hank threw his hands in the air and said, "Hey! Class is over. You guys have got the idea! You've got it!" And he sat down with an approving grin.

Their teacher stepped to the front of the class and sat on the edge of her desk. She folded her

NOTES

arms and looked into everyone's eyes. "You amaze me. What an adult leap you have made today. My guess is that if you go home and tell your parents what you have learned and share the Ten Acre Principle with them, you are going to have more and more success as eternal families.

Their teacher also said, "I suggest that you get your pencils and write a paper on these ideas right now while it is fresh on your minds. Remember when you see, feel, touch, and hear things you retain the knowledge much better and this is too important to lose. We will have time to go over your recollections before you go home today."

Sarah Lou asked if they could think of a particular problem and write down how to handle it using the Ten Acre Principle.

"Excellent idea! Applying the principle is an excellent way to remember an idea."

The teacher lowered her chin, supported her forehead with her index finger and thoughtfully said, "Let me ask you one question. Suppose using the

NOTES

Ten Acre Principle is slow getting results here and there once in a while, what is THE ONLY OTHER THING you can do to get people to change for the good?

Students' wheels were really turning. You could see them wondering what the answer could possibly be.

The youngest student in the classroom raised her hand and said, "My Sunday School teacher said you just pray for them and love them into changing--that's all you have the right to do. The Devil tries to MAKE people change. Jesus said to be nice to them, love them, and pray for them. She says sometimes when people are acting strangely they really are just crying for help, and may only need some love and attention."

Turning to Hank the teacher said, "Hank you are so right! This class is over. You students are such bright warriors. You are not going to have much trouble in life. I'm proud to know you."

NOTES

****

Suggested Exercise

Q. What constitutes YOUR ten acres?

List the things that fall on your ten acres?

Q. Are you as an individual ready to answer for your actions on your ten acres?

Q. Will you be more considerate of those who share a three acres with you?

Q. Will understanding this principle help you to think carefully before you try to change another person, or step into their business without being asked, or given permission?

Q. Do you have some good ideas now about how to communicate with anyone with whom you disagree?

Q. Will you practice the Ten Acre Principle in your life?

Q. Do you feel comfortable introducing this way to solve problems to your family?

NOTES

TREES WE DIDN'T PLANT

We can look to pioneer days to gain appreciation for the present and perspective for the future.

Let us look also upon the virtues of those wonderful pioneers to gain strength for whatever lies ahead of us, and to increase our gratitude for blessings. What are some blessings they had that WE MAY NOT HAVE?

It is good to reflect upon the work of those who labored so hard and gained so little in this world, but out of whose dreams and early plans, so well nurtured, has come a great harvest of which we are the beneficiaries. It may be said that we are enjoying the shade, the coolness, the blessings of trees we did not plant!

NOTES

Today we honor the past and the present pioneers in our own areas.

Let's take a look at some of their privations, their lack of plenty, and see how they met those challenges. Journals and early histories such as was written by Brother George F. Shelly, give us various pictures of those times and seasons.

EARLY HOMES

What happens when Dad comes home and says "We're going to move to another home!" Does what follows next happen to us?

When pioneers arrived in the valley their wagons continued to be their homes for months! Eventually they dug into the side of a hill, or into the ground and then covered the dugout with branches and crude mud coverings. When they were able to build a log house and chink the cracks with mud, they still had dirt floors to live on.

NOTES

TRAVEL

How long does it take your family to arrive in Salt Lake City from your home? It used to take at least two days to travel from Provo to Salt Lake City. They traveled on dirt, rutted roads in bumpy, horse drawn wagons or buggies if several people went along. It was hot or very cold, rainy, windy or dusty.

HOME FURNISHINGS

Home furnishings were scant. Very few items were brought across the plains. One mother who clung to her kitchen range (stove) she had made room for in the wagon. Finally she had to leave it out on the plains when a young girl's leg was crushed and she needed space in a wagon to finish the journey. The girl was able to walk into the valley on her own two feet because of the ride she received in a wagon. What do you suppose the lady cooked on when she moved into her mud house? Yes, a fireplace.

Crude tables, stools, beds and other equipment were made from local materials. Wooden slats,

NOTES

or ropes or rawhide substituted for bed springs which were drawn across the bed frames and cinched up when they sagged. Hay or straw on the bed or floor served as mattresses. Spinning wheels that had not made it across the plains had to be hand made.

WATER

Water was drawn from wells and if your property was near a running spring you were lucky. What if you had to walk a block down the street to get a bucket of water to drink or wash up?

There were no pipes through which the water would run into your home, much less heated, piped water! No hot running water for showers! A number two size galvanized tub was your bathtub, or else you used the creek or irrigation ditch!

LIGHTING

Their lighting system was "the flame from the fireplace and a saucer of grease, in which was placed a rag with a button on the end and the rag set aflame. This was called a "bitch" light." Later candles

NOTES

were made and used before the wonderful kerosene lamp came into use. Kerosene was scarce and the lanterns had to be used with care to keep from exploding.

HEATING

Fires were made with wood hauled from the cedars west of the Jordan River, from the "Big Patch" in the west hills. This area was more accessible because there were few roads into any of the canyons for a long time.

Chopping wood provided excellent winter exercise for the men and boys of the household. Gradually coal was introduced from the Coalville mines.

How many of you know how to chop wood? What is so special about knowing how to chop wood? Ask a Boy Scout who has had fire making! A person has to learn to stand a certain way to hit the wood from the right angle in order that the ax will swing between the legs if it misses the block of wood. What would happen if the ax missed the

NOTES

wood? Yes, you might cut your foot off!

FOOD

Providing food was a major problem. Families were large and having six to ten or more children was not unusual. Balanced diets were not even considered! The problem was to provide enough food to satisfy hunger. Several times it was recorded in personal journals that the Lord provided manna on the sides of the hills just as He did for the Saints of Bible days. Manna grew on the outskirt hills in Tooele for a season or two in early years.

Grasshopper trouble in 1856, 1870 and 1879 and a drought for several years made food supply scarce. Sego Lilies, thistle roots, various kinds of greens were used to supplement a pretty good supply of fish and game. "The eating of too much fish and game made some of the people ill, so flour and vegetables were in demand. Flour at one time was $20 per hundred pounds."

After Johnston's Army came to Cedar Valley, residents in Cedar Fort made a little money raising

NOTES

vegetables for the soldiers.

Corn meal was extensively used for mush and making corn bread known as corn dodger or johnny cake. Bread and milk suppers were very common.

Molasses made of beets, carrots and water-melons, and a little later made from sorghum cane was common. Home made butter and cheese were used, but it was considered criminal extravagance to use more than one item on your bread at a time! What? No peanut butter and jam!

Among food luxuries was blood puddings, custard puddings, tripe, and chitlings (fat after the grease is rendered out of it). Later the Saints were taught that the consumption of blood was an evil practice.

CLOTHING

Before the spinning wheel and loom became more available, most people, especially men, wore buckskin, elk skin and buffalo skin clothing. These were used for bedding as well. Soon some did custom work on their wheels and looms to provide

NOTES

cloth for clothing.

"The early dress hung in a straight line from the neck to the ankles. Later came the hooped skirts and contracted waists."

FOOT WEAR

Moccasins were common footwear, but it was not unusual for women and children to go barefoot in the summer. Many children and women walked across the plains barefooted.

Shoes were scarce and usually home made. A few people had what were called shoe "lasts". These were iron molds that looked like the soles of a shoe and mounted upside down on top of a standing iron piece so you could fit leather to its size. After the sole was cut, leather was cut to go around the top part of the foot. The two pieces then could be nailed or sewn together while mounted on the last.

"Happy were the young men and women who could wear a number five shoe on a number seven foot. Boots were common in the early days, but getting the boots off and on in the winter time was a

NOTES

serious problem, requiring boot jacks and much manual strength."

Outlying farm wives knitted stockings for the soldiers in Cedar Valley also. This again helped them financially.

HEALTH CARE

Plain food, plenty of exercise and an outdoor life promoted physical health.

You may recall that Brother Brigham Young promised the saints who walked across the plains with handcarts that barring accidents, etc. they would be healthier when they arrived in the Valley than when they began their journey! Why did it take us so long to find out walking was that good for us?

Home nursing and the use of various herbs became common practice. "If a cold came, hop tea was used. If a fever arose, garden sage might be the remedy; if measles appeared, Nannie berries..." and if a baby was born, the midwife was called.

The midwife cooked and cared for the whole family, the delivery, and a ten day stay for $5.00.

NOTES

Early on, President Snow went with the Relief Society president into the Wards and Stakes to ask for volunteers to come to Salt Lake and learn midwifery in a 3-week course. Later a 6-week course was offered, then other doctoring was introduced for the care of flu, broken bones, etc.. This instruction took three months, then a few years later, six months. But on the whole, midwives did most of the doctoring as physicians were very limited.

"Healing by faith was very much in evidence then, and unskilled people who were handy with pinchers took the place of dentists."

BAPTISM

Where do people in your family get baptized?

When do they get baptized?

For a long time in outlying areas baptisms were done in ditches which were dammed up. Then as baptismal fonts were built children and others had arrangements to come in every year or two for baptisms. In Utah County they came into the new

NOTES

Alpine Tabernacle in American Fork every two years for baptisms for a long while. As in other communities, all of Utah County was one stake, Alpine Stake, for a long time.

Pioneers were grateful for what they had and gave thanks for such meager things. We have so much. Do we tell Heavenly Father thank you often enough?

(All quoted statements come from The History of American Fork, by George F. Shelley. The book is out of print.)

****

Suggested Exercise

1. Go to each heading and ask yourself what you would do to provide temporary shelter, food, clothing, warmth, etc. in the event an earthquake left you without these necessities.
2. Write your answers in your journal. It will be fun to see what you can come up with in emergencies. You could be the one to have to live with your answers, so think this through carefully.
3. Do you have a 72-hour Kit?
4. What is in it?
5. Is it, or one large enough to accommodate the whole school in order and at school in case you needed it there?
6. Talk about is needed at school, and set up a plan to get a 72-hour Kit ready for school.

The following story provides the opportunity to develop vocabulary. High school junior and senior students who are interested in writing, doing in-depth research, or having a verbal advantage will want to participate in this lesson. Find definitions for the difficult or unfamiliar words and rewrite the story in your own words using more familiar terms. A thesaurus may be helpful to some.

NOTES

THE PRINCIPLE OF FAMILY ORIGIN

"What makes a family? What are the 'family values' we hear so much about? Are they the same values Latter-day Saints understand and should hold fast?"

Brother Bradley walked back and forth slowly before his class of young adults. He had developed problem solving with this small group by exercising their mental capacities. He used the cause and effect reasoning so many times, and the students loved getting into a session now and again.

"Let me ask you further, could there have been a first family without two individuals who could produce offspring, or reproduce? Perpetuation of the family, or reproduction, is the principle of family

NOTES

origin, is it not?"

"Only in reproducing could there have occurred the love and bonding of family cohesiveness." George, a Family Living student spoke up with a redundant observation, "But any man can become a father...can reproduce!"

His professor offered an additional point of view, "That observation has value, but what kind? Is it foreign to values that count? Wouldn't you say that just the ability to reproduce is self gratification? Isn't that falling short of the desired result--why do we want children? What is the point?"

Brother Bradley was not interested in promoting sophistry or intellectualizing per se. He wanted them to use their capacities to think and to reason while using gospel principles to identify good and evil.

From the back of the room came a slow, measured response, "I call that human nature, which evidences bonding or caring and not just lust, an amazing love." A small red haired girl on the back

NOTES

row spoke with conviction. She continued, "Therefore those characteristics which bond and build a unit or a family of love, trust and accountability, I think, can be propagated, and can be referred to as true family values."

Brother Bradley picked up on her apparent thought provoking reflections.

"I see you have been giving this some real thought, Jenny. What else have you been thinking?"

"Well, values--the valid, positive kind--weld and support cohesiveness. Those values support an amazing love."

Class could be dull and uninteresting some-times, but today George and R.J. found their instructor covering the very topic they had hashed over the night before when two men had come into the malt shop and began to promote a certain line of conversation that made them uncomfortable . The redhead in the back was no dummy on the subject. Her head was on straight! George too had given this trend of thought some time... from a man's point of

NOTES

view, of course.

"These elements Jenny speaks of are only optimum--and the family unit is at its best--only when it operates with positive goals, with the intention of, and ability to breed honesty, honor, decency, and....the principles of origin!"

This was great! These students were in a thinking mode today. Brother Bradley wondered if he could pull it all together letting them do it from their responses?

"Breeding? Jennie, can you breed character traits?"

"Well, when genuine affection exists, "bre-eding" of honesty, honor, and decency is done through example, I think. Reciprocal love and respect make offspring want to follow the examples set. I know that people are not perfect all the time, but by nature alone, we have opposition in the trying and failing." Jenny shifted in her seat and flipped her long hair over her shoulder.

R.J., believed what his father had taught him.

NOTES

"We also have opposition in negative examples. Bad examples sure help us to choose knowingly which example will bring the desired results--you know, of producing more love and respect or no love, and disrespect."

"What kind of components are we talking about here? You say we must have opposition in all things, but what makes up this love, this cohesiveness?" Brother Bradley baited their thoughts.

George jumped at the chance to explain, "Values which support the togetherness of a family, must be made up of components such as trust. This brings together and preserves the integrity of the family."

He hurried on, "A family cannot be preserved as a loving and caring unit, if one or more contrary or negative principles eat away at the root or the body of the family. Boy, it is easy to see when a family is breaking down and falling apart!"

"So, George, negative values are those which break down, subvert and overthrow the principles of

NOTES

origin. Negative values can and do operate as a unit also though. What about that?"

Brother Bradley rubbed his chin as if to say they needed to do some more figuring. "What is the difference between positive and negative values?"

R.J. raised his hand, "Their elements are different. They are distrust, and are without accountability, and have no lasting cohesiveness. In that case the enduring strength of amazing love is totally absent. What the negative caliber of values produces--the ones the world talks about--is not that amazing love!"

Jenny picked up on this one. "The world says that everyone's values are different, that they are what the individual makes them. That is true all right, but they sometimes leave their measuring sticks behind! Values are only worth having if they are built on gospel truths. I wouldn't put much value on some practices I see!"

Jenny started curling her hair around her finger but elaborated just the same. "Instead, negative

NOTES

values are *conditional* affection or devotion. This type of love is eventually eroded when conditions are not met or integrity is faced head on.

"Think of the gangster family as an extreme example: They may have guarded respect or love for each other but in their suspect relationship one violation ends with somebody getting a cement casket at the bottom of the river. There is no forgiveness, or tolerance or love when mistakes are made."

"Yes, we know," said Brother Bradley, "that life with a natural, even fierce but healthy opposition, does sometimes leave the family unit fragmented. What about when a mistake, or violation of family rules occur? What happens when through an accident, lets say, an impairment of one or more of its members occurs? What then? Is retention of that bond and the respect for family ties kept alive and thriving? Does understanding bridge the impasse; can the family come even more closely together? If need be, is it through other members of the family

NOTES

that the perpetuation of the principles of origin come or continue."

Jenny again added, "My mother says we are just naturally drawn to look for and evaluate the traits in others that will bring families together. The traits or values which venerate that wonderful, sustaining, amazing love are the ones I think girls look for in the fellows they want to marry."

"The family that can always count on the honesty of its members will stick together," said R.J. who got up and went to the chalk board, asking permission. "May I...?" he said picking up the chalk. He wrote in large dramatic longhand on the board, "The honesty value is powerful, and carries with it impeccable worth and unblemished reputation!"

R.J. turned to look at the class and grinned, "My dad made me memorize this when I was twelve!"

Everyone chuckled. R. J. raised his hand to check the class, "Wait! There is more!" Then he continued to write on the board, "Ultimately no

NOTES

ravage can destroy the honest person. The dishonest person may shatter others for a while, but not in the long run."

The small class roared with yeas and applause while R.J. returned to his seat. "Took me a long time to turn those memorized words into real meaning for me."

George said to him, "You knew memorizing that would come in handy some day, didn't you?"

Brother Bradley paused till the laughter quieted and asked seriously, "What is the real difference between honesty and dishonesty?"

It was Jenny again with Julia adding her comments along the way.

"The difference between the two is integrity.... Dishonesty is negative, faulty, and washes away, always having to be reorganized."

"Honesty is positive, it prevails, and stands the ravages of lesser values." Julia said, "Someone said it is better to be trusted than to be loved! How would it feel to be loved but never trusted?"

NOTES

Brother Bradley this time stepped to the chalkboard. "Probably the most encompassing family values are:

1. Accountability and honesty, he wrote. He turned to the class and elaborated, "They become elusive to those who have never been taught positive values, or whose values have broken down. These people have to be taught what the different applications of dishonesty are and adopt a strong commitment to honesty.

"It is dishonest to steal time from your friends, employer, from your family or parents, church, community, or nation." He asked the class, for practice, to name three examples for each position.

"It is dishonest to cheat or exploit anyone, any time, any place.

"It is dishonest to lie about any thing, any situation, any person.

Brother Bradley told a short story.
"A few years ago while visiting in another state, a situation came up wherein I was asked to falsify a

NOTES

statement. I refused, saying I could not lie about whatever it was. The other person replied, 'Boy, if it were a matter of this seriousness, I surely would!' In her mind there was a good enough cause or reason to lie. Don't we all sometimes think this?

"My answer was that I did not know how the matter would be resolved, but it would have to come about another way, that I would never be comfortable lying about it.

"It was not three days until we received word that the matter had been resolved and everything was in order.

"You see, I did not need to bear false witness. Heavenly Father worked it out for me."

Their instructor asked, "Is it dishonest to promise anything you know you cannot, will not, or may not be able to produce?" The class nodded.

"Accountability and honesty promote character, steadfastness, and an ever increase in trust, love and respect.

2. What does morality encompass?" Each of

NOTES

the students spoke in turns: "Standards: chastity, virtue, honor--which include faithfulness--fairness and decency."

"Yes," spoke Brother Bradley, "And the family and its members whose conduct is respectful of these principles will have cohesiveness. Each will feel comfortable that love for him is always there and being returned fairly. He will know he is respected, valued and being nurtured.

"In that caring he knows the other person is decent and has an honest sense of the principles of origin. He knows also that the other is clean in mind and body and can be physically, mentally, and spiritually dealt with happily and safely.

"Without an ongoing effort to espouse moral values, despite human regression from time to time, what happens?" asked Brother Bradley.

R.J. spoke knowingly, "That not only happens in families, but a whole nation perishes. Decay sets in and cohesiveness breaks down all over the place."

NOTES

"Fostering amazing love necessitates the maintenance of sound moral values and trustworthy behavior. There is an imposing principle that says we never stand still, we either progress or retrogress, go ahead or fall behind.

Jenny believed that being "together", although when apart, and acting for the welfare of each other as well as for self, is what family values are all about."

She said, "There are millions of good people and good families in America who have fine values, who are trying hard to cultivate those values. However, too many have been sold a bill of goods that are worthless and deceptive; and are ruining the tender shoots of youth all over the place."

"We must courageously support and defend the principles of origin. As a nation, have we swallowed the proposition that right is wrong, and wrong is right? That bad is good, and good is bad?"

One last question was posed to the class in Family Living.

NOTES

"How can we TELL WHETHER wrong is right?" Then he answered, "The Holy Ghost will prompt us that wrong is negative, will not stand up to scrutiny, is faulty, deceptive, lives in darkness, raises red flags to the righteous, and washes away the underpinning of the family.

The following are three important clues to remember about following *anyone*, even those "in authority" over us.

You are not required to do anything asked of you if it is against the law, if it violates your integrity, or if it will physically or emotionaly harm anyone.

People may change. Family values and righteous principles will not, have not.

****

Suggested Exercise

Q. Are there different sets, or kinds, of values?

Q. Would codes of conduct, or beliefs of those who espouse (accept) immorality as O.K. because "everyone is doing it", be of value to Latter-day Saints?

NOTES

Q. Why not? (Living immorally would open up a whole can of worms for LDS; it could cause us to break very important commandments, expose us to heartache, distrust, disease, guilt, and shame that we did not care for ourselves enough to hold higher values.)

Q. How could we multiply and replenish the earth if there were not a male and female marriage?

Q. We start out with baptism, but what is the most important covenant we make with Heavenly Father if we want to live in the celestial kingdom? (Celestial marriage, so if we are true to the end, we can have children in heaven to build our own kingdoms within God's kingdom.)

Q. In the third paragraph in this story, you will find the definition of the principle of family origin. What is it? (Perpetuation of the family--children having children who have children, etc.--is the principle of family origin.)

Q. You have heard of songs and scriptures that refer to "amazing grace". Which can only come to us because of Gods love for us. What is there about love that is so amazing? (The kind of love that can build in two righteous individuals sealed in a temple marriage through priesthood blessing. Sincere people want more than ever to please Heavenly Father and remain as righteous as possible so their family will be forever.)

Q. What is "natural affection"?
(A spiritual fondness, tenderness, and love held for life and for

NOTES

loved ones.)

Q. What happens when a person no longer has natural affection? (They have no regard (respect) for others or the feelings of others, nor for life itself.)

Q. Can people who run in gangs with the intent of being a law unto themselves, have a healthy natural affection?

Q. What do negative values produce?
(Distrust, no honor, no lasting love, no loyalty; they eat away at the good things like friends, family, etc. Read again what Jenny said about "conditional" affection.)

Q. How can you identify positive, or righteous values? (They build love and trust, don't tear down.)

Q. Discuss the importance of honesty. Is it better to be trusted than to be loved? Why? (Check out again what R.J.'s father had him to memorize, and which R.J. wrote on the chalk-board.)

Q. Is it ok to even tell little "white" lies? Why?

Q. Beside the "it is O.K. to be violent" value, what other value can ruin a whole nation?
(The negative value of being immoral has overthrown many nations before...even Israel!)

Q. In the next-to-last paragraph what does the Holy Ghost tell us about negative values?

Communicate With Our Hearts Through Prayer.

NOTES

WHAT IS YOUR HEART CONDITION?

The Lord is interested in the condition of our hearts. We are his children. He loves us. What is the condition of your heart?

We speak not about our physical heart, but our spiritual heart and where we stand with regard to his greatest commandments. He said there are no greater commandments than that we love him and one another--and that we even love our enemies!

The New Testament is replete with sound and encouraging incentives to apply the redeeming principle of love: "Do good to them which hate you...Bless them that curse you...Pray for them which despitefully use you...Lend to them without hoping for `nothing again' (in return)...Be

NOTES

merciful...Judge not." Are these impossible commandments? Does the Lord really expect us to do these things? Yes. He does.

Paul (Romans 13) counsels that "Love worketh no ill to his neighbor: therefore love is the fulfilling of the law (to love one another)." The first commandment is to love the Lord, and throughout his word he commands that we love one another. We cannot successfully keep the commandment to love without doing away with negative communication, and building close, harmonious relationships.

We cannot individually compare our progress with any other. We have to stand on our own record in the light of our own weaknesses and strengths.

In Galatians 5:22 we are told, "But the fruit of the Spirit is love, joy, peace, long-suffering, gentleness, goodness, faith, meekness, temperance.

In the earnest evaluation of our capacity to love as we ought, we might ask ourselves when we last read the greatest of all sermons on pride? (ENSIGN,

NOTES

MAY 1989, by President Benson) Remember what an impact that had on all of us? Did we dream pride had or could strip us of real love?

For example: How often do we contend with a fellow worker, a school mate, our neighbor or family members? Is it contending to pursue a course, an idea or action, without allowing a neighbor to have a different course, idea, or action? When we have disagreed, did our love allow them the privilege of disagreeing? And did our love allow them time to grow, or to change, or even remain in their present state of mind, while we patiently just kept on loving them?

Are we giving in to contention when we harbor resentment in our hearts? Can we keep gossip to ourselves, and not talk to others about it? Probably not. How often do we talk about an unrequited love, or an unresolved incident *with parties who are not involved?* In other words, do we gossip? Whether or not the truth is told (according to our belief) hurt is prolonged by repeating most negative experiences

NOTES

to anyone. Repeating tends to breed strife and more contention.

There is only one time when repeating a questionable incident is legitimate and that is when we are seeking counsel, not just visiting.

Nephi tells us (Fourth Nephi 1:15) if we have the love of God in our hearts, there can be no contention. In Third Nephi we are told that the spirit of contention is of the devil.

Is it possible for one in charge to make an adjustment in assignments in Ward or Stake or school settings, and then repeat to others the reasons? Whatever they may be, we are chancing injury or discouragement to the one released? How could we better handle leadership responsibilities and still demonstrate patience and love for each person who has handled his calling the best he could?

How forgiving can we be? Can we personally hope to love another when that person has injured us in some way? Do we focus on our hurt, or do we

NOTES

remember the Kingdom, the Cause, and the contributions we are able to make when under the influence of the right Spirit?

"My little children," I John 3:18 tells us, "let us not love in word, neither in tongue; but in deed and in truth." Again, from Galatians, "If we live in the Spirit, let us also walk in the Spirit. Let us not be desirous of vain glory, provoking one another, envying one another...instead,...Bear one another's burdens...be not weary in well doing. ..."

An excellent way to learn to love another toward whom we have ill feelings, AND WE CAN LEARN TO LOVE ANYONE, is to take to heart the admonition to pray for the other person. If we really want to love the people we live and work with, we have to look beyond their shortcomings, or our disagreements with them, and pray for them.

Everyone's intentions are the best! Nearly everyone means well. They may not be any better than we are at executing those intentions, so we must pray that they can become the person *THEY*

NOTES

really want to be, not the person WE want them to be! The other person wants to be nice, to be loving, to be a neighbor who serves willingly. Pray diligently, with real intent, that the Lord will bless them to become just that kind of person. Secondly, we must repent of our lack of using wisdom, of being forgiving.

We can then ask the Lord to TAKE FROM US THE ILL FEELINGS we harbor in our hearts. He has that power! If we really want to be rid of an uncomfortable, cankerous, gnawing, and sick feeling toward a situation or person(s), we will pray for the person toward whom we have little or no good will, and acknowledge our own contribution to the situation. Then we will simply ask the Lord to remove from us that awful feeling. He can and he will.

Foster, develop a love and appreciation for the good in another. Someone once said that asking a favor of the one with whom we have had a problem, will show our increased confidence and faith in them, and will do wonders for demonstrating our

NOTES

willingness to forgive and forget. What a wonderful feeling it is to leave behind all thoughts and conversations of negativeness, and to put into practice love and caring for the good things, the good habits, the kindnesses of others. They have them. We know they do. We may not have been seeing them while we had hate or disgust, revenge or pride in our own hearts.

"God is love; he that dwelleth in love dwelleth in God and God in him." I John 4:16. Let us pray that we can be submissive to the spirit of love, the best of good heart conditioning programs!

****

Suggested Exercise

1. Tell what Paul means when he said to the Romans that "love worketh no ill".

2. Fourth Nephi 1:15 if we have.......in our hearts there can be no contention. What is contention?

3. If we truly want to get rid of bad feelings about any person, how do we do it? Can we do it by ourselves?

4. What keeps us from seeing good things, good habits, and the kindnesses of others?

5. Make a point of finding and reading President Ezra Taft Benson's conference talk on pride.

INDEX